INTRODUCTION: YOUR FAV

BROTHER RAGE (OUR HERO'S LOVE INTEREST'S BOYFRIEND)
THE LAST POETS
THIS IS MADNESS
(1971)
THIS RECORD IS THE MOST IMPORTANT RECORD OF ALL TIME! IF YOU'RE WHITE, IT'LL SCARE THE S#!T OUTTA YOU. IF YOU'RE BLACK, IT'LL SCARE THE NIGGA OUTTA YOU!

DEXTER (OUR HERO'S OLDER BROTHER)
AWWW YEAH! DIS MY S#!T RIGHT 'CHERE! BEATS, BLUNTS AND BITCHES ALWAYS MAKE FOR A DOPE-ASS REKKID! AIN'T NOBODY DO IT LIKE LUDA! I SWURTOGAH, BRUH!
LUDACRIS
CHICKEN-N-BEER
(2003)

LEE JIM (OUR HERO'S MAILMAN)
OH MY, YES! A BIG FAN OF HERS, INDEED. AND THIS ONE MEANS A LOT TO ME. IT REPRESENTS WHEN SHE WAS SIXTEEN AND...DEVELOPING... AS AN MUSICAL ARTIST, THAT IS!
DEMI LOVATO
DON'T FORGET
(2008)

MRS. GUTIERREZ (OUR HERO'S LANDLADY)
WOW! IF THIS RECORD DOESN'T TAKE ME BACK?! I DON'T REMEMBER A MORE OUTRAGEOUS OR PROVOCATIVE OR EXCITING SOUNDTRACK TO MY DAYS AT UNIVERSITY THAN THIS BABY.
GAL COSTA
GAL COSTA
[CINEMA OLYMPIA]
(1969)

MARSALIS (OUR HERO)

AHEM!... **MARSALIS** (OUR HERO)

DUDE, GET YER ASS OUT HERE!
ALR-R-RIGHT ALREADY! I'M HERE!
f-f-fake-ass keith knight wannabe.

W-W-WELL, I MUST SAY THAT I OWE YOU READERS AN AP-P-POLOGY FOR MY LACK OF P-P-PREPAREDNESS. WHEN A WRITER CONSUMES C-C-COPIOUS AMOUNTS OF VINYL, FINDING A FAVORITE ALBUM BECOMES D-D-DIFFICULT OVER TIME.

AND PART OF THE D-D-DIFFICULTY COMES FROM ALWAYS LOOKING OUT FOR THE C-C-CLASSICS OF *TODAY*, NOT JUST F-F-FETISHIZING THE PAST. SO I SEE THAT EVERYBODY ELSE HAS *Z-Z-ZIGGED.*

THEN I SHALL *Z-Z-ZAG* AND PRESENT SOMETHING THAT'S TODAY *AND* TOMORROW. THIS G-G-GEM CONTAINS PERHAPS THE MOST C-C-CUTTING, PRECISE BARS OF PUSHA-T'S CAREER. ONLY SEVEN SONGS AND 21 MINUTES, IT'S QUITE THE M-M-MASTERPIECE OF HIP-HOP MINIMALISM.
PUSHA-T *DAYTONA* (2018)

if y-y-you ask me, it looks kinda p-p-pitiful worshipping the same 40-50 year-old records that everybody already knows are g-g-great. there's s-s-something braver and nobler in looking ahead.

THE F%$K IS HE CALLING PITIFUL?!

BLACKWAX BOULEVARD:
FIVE YEARS, WHAT A SURPRISE
(2012–2017)

table of contents

MFG. BY FROTOON PRESS.

#1

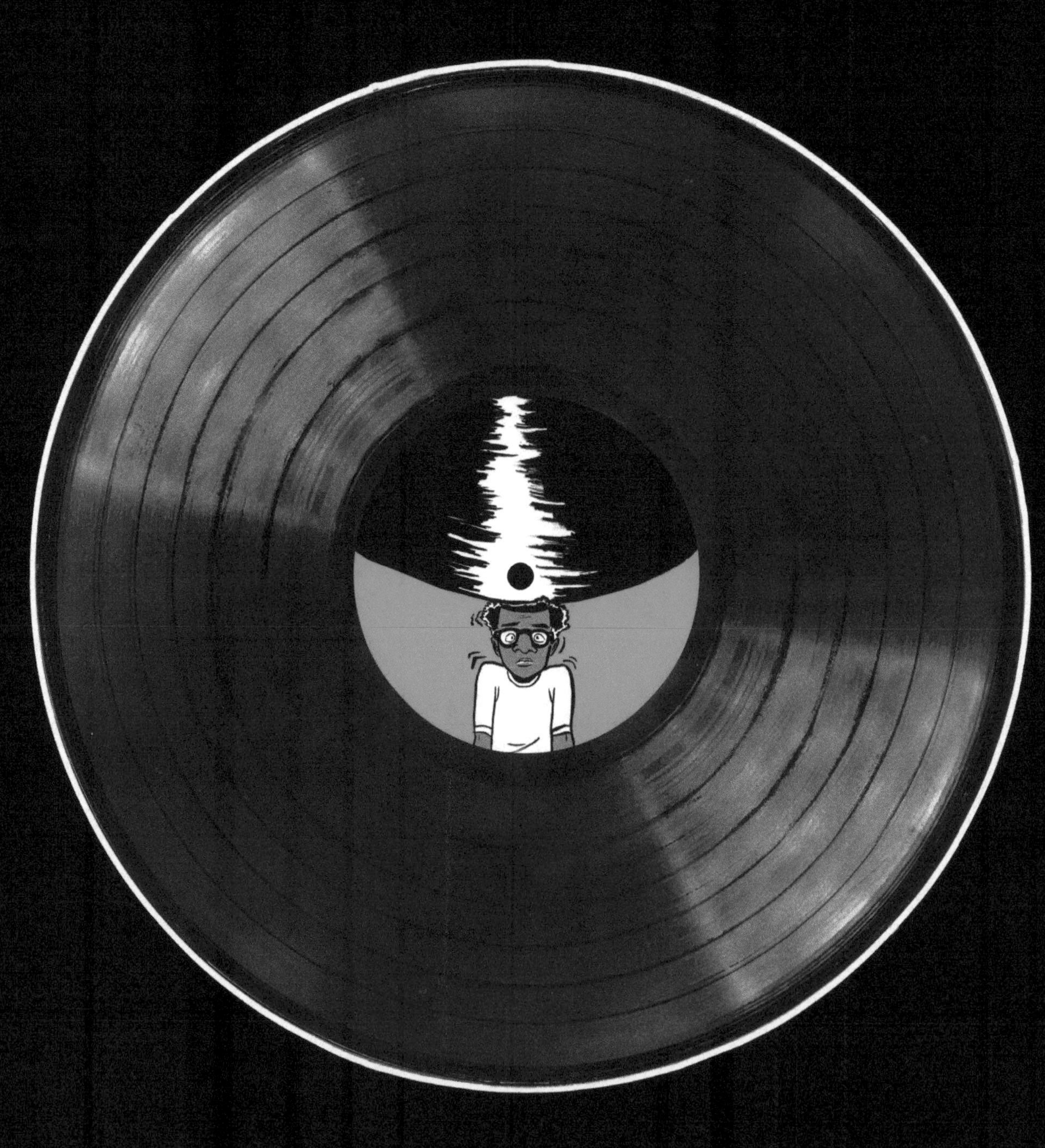

OK. S-S-SO LET ME MAKE SURE I G-G-GOT THIS RIGHT: YOU WOULD RATHER SPEND YOUR HARD EARNED MONEY BUYING A L-L-LAME CHRISTOPHER CROSS CD THAN PRETZEL LOGIC?
MARSALIS J. PARKER (CLERK)
LOOK, I ALREADY TOLD YOU! I JUST DON'T LIKE STEELY DAN! THEIR SONGS ARE TOO ARCANE AND THEY LOOK LIKE HIPPIES!

BUT THAT'S WHAT MAKES THEM G-G-GENIUS! THEY ASK YOU TO GIVE THEIR SONGS YOUR F-F-FULL ATTENTION, TO PONDER AND DECODE THEIR MEANING. THEY'RE NOT THERE TO JUST C-C-CONSUME. YOU CONSUME AND YOU'LL ALSO M-M-MISS A LOTTA THE IRONIC HUMOR IN THE WORDS.

WELL, NOT ALL MUSIC HAS TO MAKE YOU THINK, YOU KNOW. AND I GET WHAT HE'S SINGING ABOUT. BESIDES, A CATCHY MELODY'S ALL I REALLY WANT.

SO YOU'LL B-B-BUY AN ALBUM DEVOID OF C-C-CATCHY MELODIES? THIS ISN'T EVEN HIS D-D-DEBUT FROM '79. AT LEAST THAT ONE'S GOT S-S-SOME GOOD STUFF.

NO, I HATE THAT ONE. SOUNDS TOO ABRASIVE.

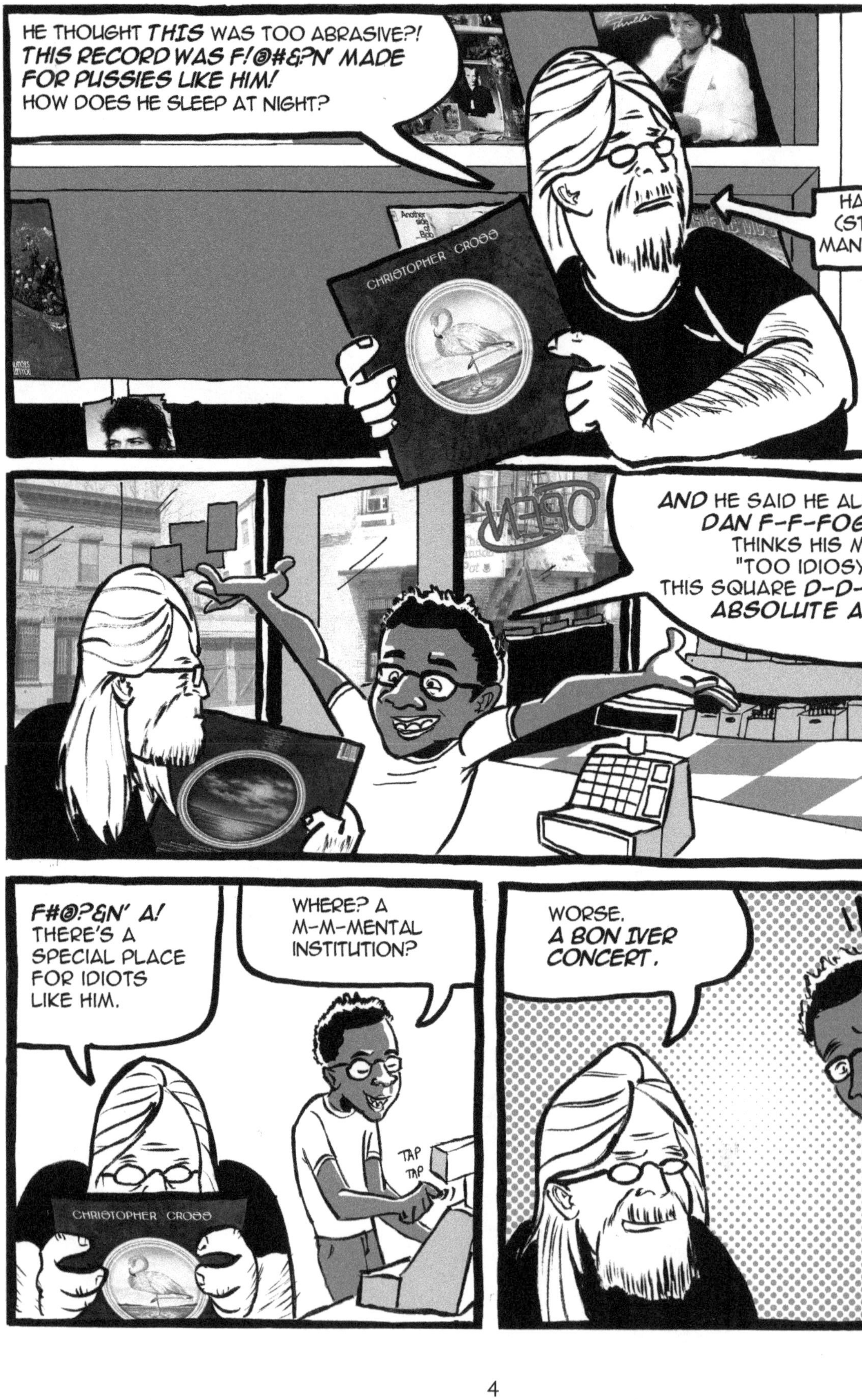

HE THOUGHT *THIS* WAS TOO ABRASIVE?!
THIS RECORD WAS F!@#&?N' MADE FOR PUSSIES LIKE HIM!
HOW DOES HE SLEEP AT NIGHT?

HARDY (STORE MANAGER)

CHRISTOPHER CROSS

AND HE SAID HE ALSO HATES ***DAN F-F-FOGELBERG.***
THINKS HIS MUSIC WAS "TOO IDIOSYNCRATIC."
THIS SQUARE ***D-D-DEFINES ABSOLUTE ASININITY!***

MADONNA
Thriller
CHRISTOPHER CROSS
NEW SHIPMENTS
HOW CAN YOU KNOCK B-B-BON IVER?! AND PUT HIM ON TH-TH-THE SAME LEVEL AS *CROSS AND FOGELBERG*?! HE'S FAR SUPERIOR TO THAT '70S SOFT ROCK CR-CR-CRAP!

RIGHT, *BY RECYCLING THAT '80S SOFT ROCK CRAP.*

BUT CH-CH-CHECK HIS SONG ARRANGEMENTS. THERE'S NOTHING "S-S-SAFE" ABOUT THEM. WAY MORE DIMENSION AND EXPERIMENTATION IN HIS MUSIC THAN YOU THINK. AND HE'S ALSO N-N-NOT WRITING GENERIC STATEMENTS ON LOVE. HIS LYRICS ARE SO RICH THEY DEMAND THEIR OWN *P-P-POETRY CLASS!*

LYRICS? SO THAT'S WHAT YOU CALL ALL THAT PISSING AND WHINING.

HEY, SO WHAT IF BON IVER M-M-MUMBLES? A LOTTA ARTISTS HAVE UNINTELLIGIBLE LYRICS. JUST P-P-PLAY ANY OF YOUR DEATH METAL RECORDS. THAT WHOLE G-G-GENRE'S AN EXERCISE IN UNINTELLIGIBILITY.

HEY MAN! DON'T HATE ON DEATH. THAT S#!T'S ABOUT EMOTION. AT LEAST YOU'RE FORCED TO RESPOND TO IT.

MY EARS B-B-BLEEDING TO THAT CANNIBAL CORPSE JUNK YOU ALWAYS PLAY? THAT'S RESPONDING TO IT.

CANNIBAL CORPSE ARE F#@!&?N' ROCK DEITIES, MAN! WAY MORE IMPORTANT THAN THE S#!T OUT THERE NOW! THEY'RE BETTER THAN METALLICA!

HA! THAT HURDLE'S N-N-NOT SO HIGH ANYMORE. AFTER "LULU," ANYTHING'S B-B-BETTER THAN METALLICA.

folk / world
classical
EXCUSE ME SIR, I AM EXPERIENCING TROUBLE LOCATING YOUR COLLECTION OF *SVERKENJÜVEN*.
UH, WHAT N-N-NOW?
GO DEXTER GORDON

SVERKENJÜVEN? THEY'RE, LIKE, ***THE MOST IMPORTANT DANISH VIKING METAL BAND IN THE HISTORY OF DANISH VIKING METAL! HELLO?!*** AS HEAD OF THEIR FAN CLUB, I ***DEMAND*** TO BE PROPERLY DIRECTED TO YOUR COLLECTION!

OK-K-KAY, SIR. SIMMER DOWN. OUR M-M-METAL SECTION IS PRETTY B-B-BIG. BUT I'M NOT QUITE P-P-POSITIVE THAT WE CARRY SUCH A S-S-SPECIFIC GENRE AS TH-TH-THAT. YOU MIGHT B-B-BE ABLE TO FIND WHAT YOU'RE LOOKING F-F-FOR IN CDS. BUT IF YOU CAN'T, CH-CH-CH-CHECK THE V-V-V-V---

NEVER MIND! I'LL LOOK FOR MYSELF.
F&#@!N' WEIRDO.
-V-V-VINYL SECTION.
GO DEXTER GORDON

folk / world
classical
DO YOU HAVE THE WHO'S *MY GENERATION* ON VINYL?
SALIMAH (PATRON)

?
UH, S-S-SURE. WE G-G-GOT ALL KINDS OF WHO STUFF. THE V-V-VINYL ROCK SECTION IS THAT SECOND AISLE FROM THE R-R-RIGHT.

folk / world
classical
HA! YOU'RE CUTE! MIMICKING ROGER DALTREY'S STUTTER. THANKS.
B-B-BUT I'M NOT --
SHE THINKS I'M CUTE?

NO, MARSALIS! I DON'T HAVE TIME TO DEBATE YOU. PLEASE JUST STOCK THESE CDS. I GOTTA GET THIS BACKROOM IN ORDER, QUICK!
LOOK, VERONIKA, I'M J-J-JUST SAYING IT'S A LITTLE DESPERATE TO SHIFT OUR CD ORDERS TO MORE D-D-DANCE-POP FOR BETTER SALES. THIS STORE IS ON ITS L-L-LAST LEG.
VERONIKA (INVENTORY)
WE COULD AT LEAST G-G-GO OUT WITH A SHRED OF DIGNITY AND G-G-GET SOME ROCK.

TAKE THAT UP WITH HARDY. HE'S THE MASTERMIND WHO ORDERED THIS CRAP.
NOW GO!

ALRIGHT, THEN. BUT D-D-DON'T GO B-B-BLAMING ME IF THE STORE C-C-CLOSES BECAUSE OF THIS G-G-GARBAGE.

BECAUSE THE LAST TH-TH-THING PEOPLE WILL THINK IS "RIHANNA KILLED BLACKWAX WITH HER UMBRELLA-ELLA-ELLA!" TH-TH-THAT STUTTER WAS INTENTIONAL.

blackwax boulevard

HEY, IS THIS A NEW GREEN DAY SONG?!
SEUNG-JIN (PATRON)
SHHH! NO, SEUNG-JIN, THAT'S--
IT MUST BE AN ELECTRO REMIX!

BILLIE JOE'S VOICE KEEPS STUTTERING!
THAT'S WHAT I'M TRYING TO SAY IS--

I WANT TO BE-BE-BE THE MINORITY!!! I DON'T NEED YOUR AUTHORITY-TY-TY-TY-TY-TY-TY!!!

THAT'S BECAUSE THE CD PLAYER IN THE LISTENING POST IS BROKEN AND YOU SHOULDN'T USE IT YET!
WHOOOOOOSH

OK. SHEESH, YOU DON'T HAVE TO YELL.

WHY DON'T YOU TRY ANOTHER LISTENING POST, SEUNG-JIN? THEN AFTER THAT, GET BACK TO SCHOOL BEFORE YOU GET IN TROUBLE...AGAIN!
NAH, IT'S, UH, RECESS TIME AT SCHOOL NOW, VERONIKA. AND I LIKE THIS POST ANYHOW.

GREEN DAY SHOULD GO ELECTRO. THEY SOUND COOLER WHEN THEY STUTTER. LIKE LADY GAGA.

I GUESS I'M C-C-COOL LIKE G-G-GAGA, EH? PLUS, MY STUTTER COMES WITHOUT S-S-STUDIO TRICKERY.

PROBABLY ABOUT AS COOL AS A CARTOON PIG WITH A BOWTIE AND NO PANTS. TH-TH-THAT'S ALL FOLKS!!

HA HA HA HA HA HA
HEY, M-M-MISS THANG, LOONEY TUNES ARE A C-C-CULTURAL INSTITUTION! I'LL TAKE IT AS A C-C-COMPLIMENT!

"TALK THAT T-T-TALK", EH, RIHANNA? YOU MEAN, WHATEVER THAT C-C-COMMITTEE THAT CONTROLS YOUR WHOLE IMAGE T-T-TELLS YOU TO SAY? THE COMPUTERS THAT D-D-DO YOUR SINGING? OR WHAT THAT JACKASS CALVIN HARRIS T-T-TELLS YOU TO SING?
pop/rock

OR THE BLACK LEATHER AND F-F-FISHNETS THEY TELL YOU TO WEAR? THAT B-B-BLAZING CRIMSON HAIR?

THAT GLISTENING T-T-TONGUE THAT LOVINGLY CARESSES YOUR UPPER LIP?

THAT PIERCING STARE OF DEEP HUNGER...
... FOR A L-L-LONELY BOY'S FLESH?

EH, T-T-TALK IS CHEAP.

I'M SORRY, MAN, BUT THAT RECORD'S BEEN OUT OF PRINT FOR A LONG-ASS TIME. SHERLOCK COULDN'T EVEN FIND THAT S#!T....WELL, YEAH, WE GOT COMEDY RECORDS, BUT ***I HEARD IT AT THE BARBERSHOP*** IS A TOUGH FIND.

AL SPARKS ONLY MADE THAT ONE RECORD, MAN....I KNOW IT'S A CLASSIC! ***WE ALL DO!*** BUT......BUT YOU COULD GO TO ***ANY*** BARBERSHOP IN TOWN AND HEAR THE SAME S#!T FOR FREE!

WHAT? THE ONLY BARBERSHOP IN TOWN'S ***KOREAN***? THEY MUSTA SHUT DOWN THE OTHER ONES.

WELL, GET A F?#&!N' TRANSLATOR, DUDE!

NAH, NOT A CHANCE. PAUL'S STILL GOT SOME MORE YEARS IN HIM. HIS GENES ARE STRONGER.
WHY? 'CUZ HE'S YOUNGER THAN RINGO? THEY'RE *BOTH* OLD.

DUDE, THE MUSIC GODS WOULDN'T ALLOW IT. PAUL'S THE ONLY GOOD ONE LEFT AND THEY KNOW IT. BESIDES, IF RINGO DIED IN A STUDIO AND NO ONE'S AROUND TO HEAR HIM, WOULD HE MAKE A HEADLINE? *I THINK NOT.*

BUT PAUL'S ALREADY DEAD. REMEMBER? RINGO WINS BY DEFAULT.

HA! TOLD YA!

DUDE, THIS ANDREW JACKSON SAYS RINGO BITES THE DUST NEXT.
ADD A MR. HAMILTON AND YOU GOT A DEAL.
I'LL SEE YOU AT PAUL'S FUNERAL.
RAM

I'LL RAISE YOU BOTH $10 AND ***AN OCTUPUS'S GARDEN*** ON RINGO.

HEY MARSALIS! WANT IN ON THIS?

WHAT F-F-FOR? ***THEY'RE B-B-BOTH ALREADY DEAD ARTISTICALLY.*** IT'S A DRAW TO M-M-ME.
KID A

WELL, TH-TH-THIS BOX IS FINISHED. HEY, HARDY AND TH-TH-THOSE DWEEBS ARE BETTING ON WHICH B-B-BEATLE DIES NEXT. WANT IN?
employees only
REALLY?! I MEAN, IS THAT NECESSARY?
MEN WILL TURN ANYTHING, EVEN SOMEONE DYING, INTO A CHANCE TO GET RICH!
PAUL SIMON

EH, IT'S PRETTY MUCH EXP-P-PECTED IN A CORPORATIST SOCIETY. THE M-M-MUSIC BIZ PRACTICALLY C-C-COACHES OUR BASER INSTINCTS. AND DEATH HAS *ENORMOUS* M-M-MARKET SHARE IN MUSIC.
I'M SURE THE L-L-LABELS WERE "FEELING FINE" WHEN JOHN DIED. HIS AND THE BEATLES' RECORD SALES PROBABLY WENT THE R-R-ROOF.
I BET P-P-PAUL WAS REAL CHARMED BY THE EXTRA SIMOLEONS HE FOUND IN HIS P-P-POCKET.

WOW! DID YOU MOTHER TAKE AWAY YOUR PACIFIER TOO SOON? BECAUSE YOU'RE PERHAPS *THE BIGGEST CYNIC* I'VE EVER KNOWN.

HEY, CYNICISM HAS M-M-MARKET SHARE, TOO. THERE'D B-B-BE NO *PUNK MUSIC* WITHOUT IT.

WHY ON EARTH WOULD PAUL CHEER FOR JOHN DYING?! THEY WERE PRACTICALLY BROTHERS!

THE S-S-SAME REASON HE CHEERED MICHAEL JACKSON DYING. HE FELT LIKE HE W-W-WON. JUST IMAGINE ALL THE C-C-CASH MJ GOT OFF THEIR SONGS.
NOW THAT HE'S DEAD, PAUL CAN G-G-GET THE LAST LAUGH AND DOLLARS.

I'M SURE A PART OF PAUL DIED ALONG WITH MICHAEL AND JOHN. A PART OF ALL OF US DID. SOME OF US HUMANS CAN STILL FEEL, YOU KNOW.
AND IF PAUL AND RINGO GO, IT'LL BE A SAD DAY FOR MUSIC.

AND PETE BEST WILL BE THE HAPPIEST B-B-BASTARD ON EARTH.

POOMF
WISH I COULD SAY THAT FOR YOU, AMIGO. BUT TIME'S OF THE ESSENCE. NOW KEEP STOCKING THAT KARMIN!

V-V-VINYL?! THESE CREEPS ARE TAKING UP THE V-V-VINYL SECTION NOW?! WHERE THE HELL'S YOUR B-B-BACKBONE, HARDY?
I DON'T WANNA HEAR IT, MARS! WE ALL WANT THE STORE TO STAY AROUND, RIGHT?
AND IF THAT'S THE S#!T FOLKS ARE BUYIN', I GOTTA DO WHAT I F&?!#N' GOTTA DO.
190... WELL, THAT SUCKS.
190
ONE DIRECTION
Karmin
MADONNA

B-B-BUT 40 YEARS, HARDY! IN ALL TH-TH-THAT TIME BLACKWAX'S BEEN AROUND, WHEN HAS IT EVER FELT COMP-P-PELLED TO SELL OUT?
WHAT WOULD JIMMY THINK?
ackwax bouleva
THIS STORE IS DEDICATED TO
JIMMY "FLIP" ROLLINS

LOOK, MAN. MY UNCLE STARTED THIS JOINT WELL BEFORE THIS CITY WENT DOWN THE S#!TTER.
ackwax bouleva
(1932 - 1995)
KOREAN WAR HER

AND I APPLAUD UPHOLDING ANY HIPSTER CAUSE, BUT MY INSULIN SHOTS AIN'T GONNA PAY FOR THEMSELVES.
WE GET ANY M-M-MORE SUGARY POP MUSIC, WE'LL ALL DIE OF DIABETES.

OOPS, S-S-SORRY.

LOOK ON THE BRIGHT SIDE, MARSALIS. THAT ELECTRO MUSIC HELPS PAY FOR YOUR SPEECH THERAPY.
WOW, REALLY? MISS PO-PO-POKER FACE HELPING TO C-C-CURE MY STUTTER? WONDERFUL. ALL HAIL THE GAGA!
closed
LPs CDs TAPES

THE BULLET DON'T TASTE SO BAD ONCE YOU FINALLY BITE IT, MAN.
TAKE IT EASY, HARDY. AND GET SOME MORE TAPE FOR THAT LEG CASE.

AH, I BEEN MEANIN' TO BUY A NEW ONE.
PULP FIC

L-L-LEAVE IT TO THE SWEDISH HOUSE MAFIA. 'CUZ WE ALL KN-KN-KNOW THAT DJS HAVE REAL INSTRUMENTS TO C-C-CASE UP, RIGHT?

YOU KNOW, SWEDISH HOUSE MAFIA ARE BREAKING UP. SO YOU REALLY CAN'T BASH THEM ANYMORE.
AH, S-S-SO ONE ROACH IS SQUASHED. THERE'S STILL A HUNDRED OTHERS CR-CR-CRAWLING IN THE KITCHEN.
Green Door

YOU MEAN, ROACHES LIKE PRINCE? MICHAEL JACKSON? DAFT PUNK? LCD SOUNDSYSTEM? THEY'RE DANCE-Y TOO.

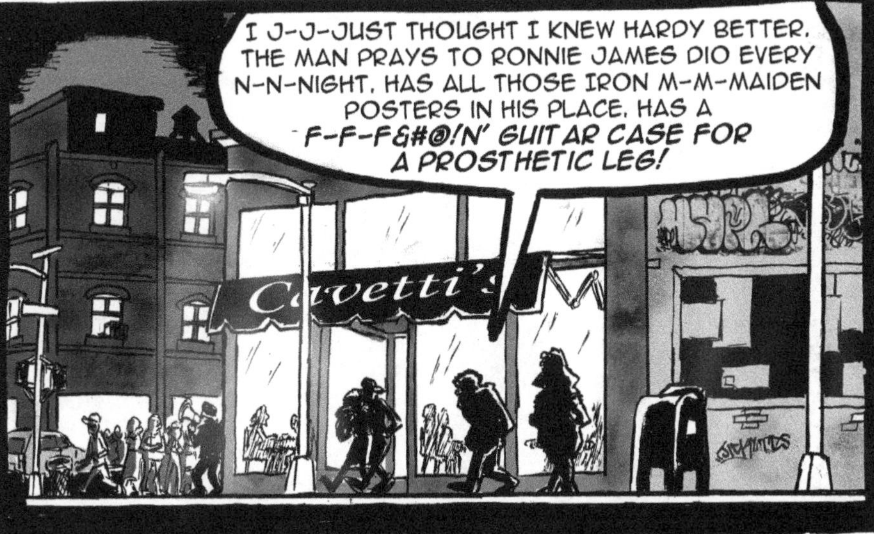
I J-J-JUST THOUGHT I KNEW HARDY BETTER. THE MAN PRAYS TO RONNIE JAMES DIO EVERY N-N-NIGHT. HAS ALL THOSE IRON M-M-MAIDEN POSTERS IN HIS PLACE. HAS A F-F-F&#@!N' GUITAR CASE FOR A PROSTHETIC LEG!
Cavetti's

HE ALSO HAS A BUSINESS TO RUN.
TR-TR-TRUE... I JUST WISH BUSINESS DIDN'T B-B-BREED SUCH CYNICISM.

IT DOES HAVE MARKET SHARE, RIGHT?
UGH...

AND I PLEAD WITH YOU, BROTHERS AND SISTERS OF GREENVILLE! WAKE UP! OPEN YOUR EYES OR WE ALL THROUGH! HOW MANY MORE CHILDREN SHALL WE LET FALL UNDER THE SPELL OF THE RED LIGHTS?!
HOW MUCH MORE BLOOD WILL WE WASH OUR STREETS WITH?! HOW MANY MORE HOMES MUST BE BROKEN BY WHITE LINES FOR YOU TO SAY ENOUGH?!?!
BROTHER RAGE

HOW M-M-MANY MORE DAVID GUETTA WANNABES MUST WE T-T-TOLERATE ON THE RADIO?!

HA HA HA HA
HA HA HA HA HA

'SCUSE ME, MY BROTHER! BUT I SENSE SOME FLIPPANCY IN YOUR SYNTAX THAT I DON'T APPRECIATE. THE ILLS OF THE STREETS ECHO THE ILLS OF THE MENTAL MIND.....

...WHICH IS BEING CULTIVATED BY THE WORLD ELITES. WE MUST INOCULATE THE DELUDED MASSES AGAINST THE ELITIST SCHEMES OF DESTRUCTION.

THEN T-T-TELL BLOGGERS TO QUIT P-P-POSTING SONGS BY KREAYSHAWN. SHE'S D-D-DELUDING WHITE GIRLS INTO THINKING THEY CAN ACTUALLY R-R-RAP.
!!!

EXCUSE ME? WHY SINGLE OUT WHITE GIRLS AS BAD RAPPERS? KREAYSHAWN ONLY LEARNS FROM GUYS LIKE B.O.B., BUN B, LIL B, LIL WAYNE, LIL JON, AND ALL THOSE OTHER DUMB RAPPERS!
LAST TIME I CHECKED MTV, THEY WERE MOSTLY BLACK.

P-P-POINT TAKEN. BUT TWO WRONGS D-D-DON'T MAKE A RIGHT. AND KREAYSHAWN AND KITTY PRYDE SURE D-D-DON'T MAKE A KANYE.

BROTHER, THE AFFLICTION OF OUR GENERATION GOES BEYOND LAME-ASS RAPPING WHITE GIRLS. ART ONLY REFLECTS OUR WORLD AT LARGE. AND IF IT'S FOUL, IT'S BECAUSE OF THE DISEASE OF CORRUPTION IN OUR GOVERNMENT, OUR WORKPLACE, OUR HOME, OUR LIVES!
IF WE CAN EXCORIATE THE PLAQUE OF COMPLACENT DISUNDERSTANDING AND ENLIGHTEN THE PEOPLE TO CHANGE WHAT'S INSIDE, THEN WE CAN CHANGE WHAT'S OUTSIDE. ONLY THEN WILL THE 1% FINALLY LOSE THEIR POWER.
YOU FEEL ME WHERE I'M COMING FROM, YOUNG BLOOD?

SIMPLY INSPIRING, BROTHER RAGE! I BELIEVE PEOPLE SHOULD ORGANIZE A MARCH ON WHAT YOU JUST SAID. THIS CITY NEEDS AN OCCUPY GREENVILLE.

AH, J-J-JUST AS WELL. THAT LENDS A B-B-BETTER TITLE, ANYWAY. OCCUPY LAME-ASS RAPPING WHITE GIRLS IS A M-M-MOUTHFUL.

WELL, MR. PARKER, THANKS FOR WALKING A GIRL HOME. I MUST SAY, THE CITY REALLY STARTS TO SCARE ME THIS TIME OF NIGHT.
HA! AS S-S-SCRAWNY AS I AM, YOU'RE ***MY*** B-B-BODYGUARD.

YOU GONNA BE SAFE GETTING BACK? MAYBE YOUR BROTHER CAN PICK YOU UP IN HIS CAB. SHOULD BE HERE SHORTLY.

NAH, THE CAB SERVICE CHANGED HIS ROUTES. I'M F-F-FINE WALKING. BESIDES, I'M SKINNY EN-N-NOUGH TO MAKE A ***CONVINCING D-D-DOPE FIEND.***

A DOPE FIEND WHO LOOKS LIKE HE CRAWLED OUT OF ***URBAN OUTFITTERS?*** HA! YOU'LL BLEND RIGHT IN.

HEY, YOU G-G-GO TO ***HOT TOPIC*** TO LOOK LIKE A D-D-DOPE FIEND. BUT YOU GO TO URBAN OUTFITTERS TO LOOK LIKE A ***D-D-DOPE!***

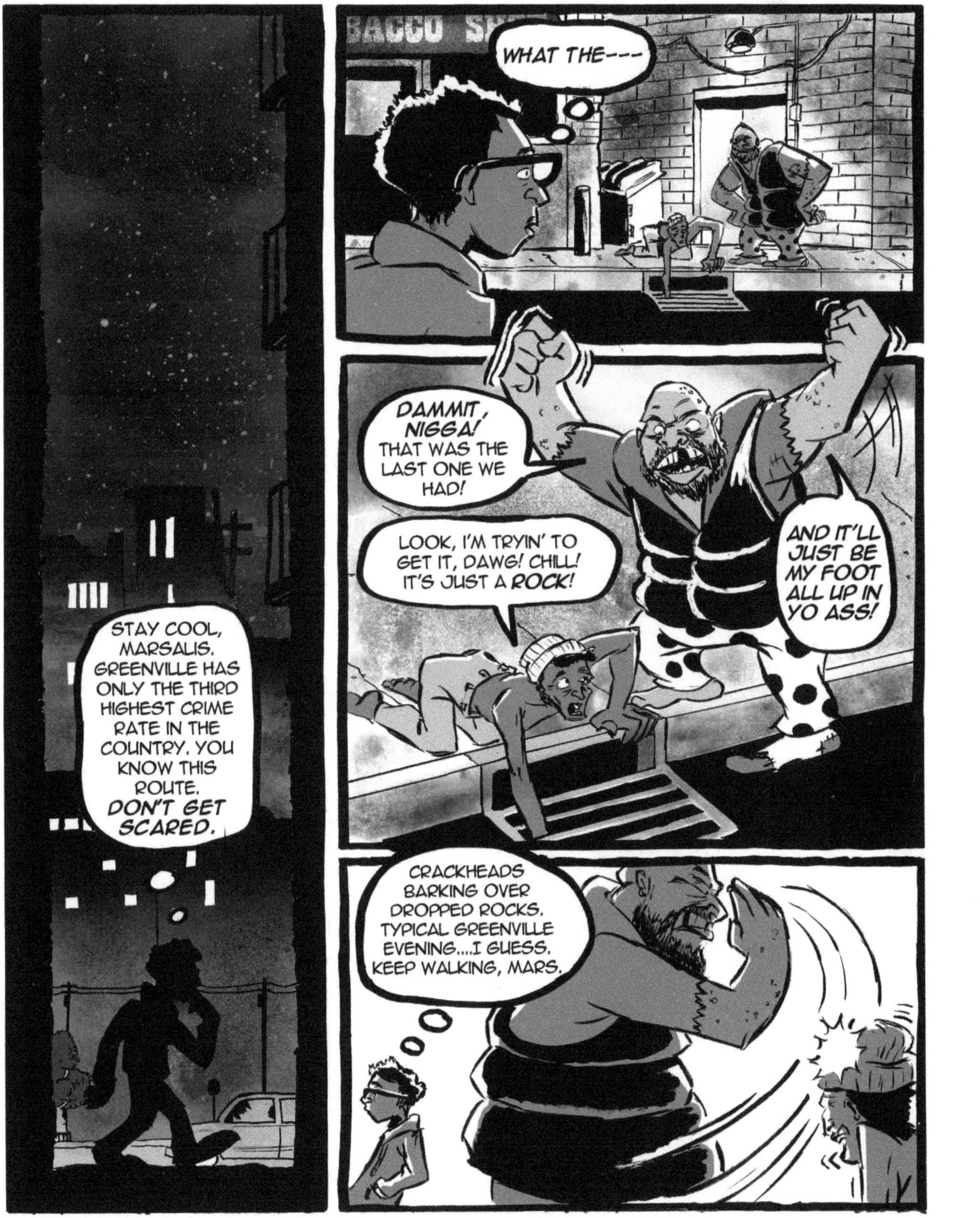

BACCO S

WHAT THE---

DAMMIT, NIGGA! THAT WAS THE LAST ONE WE HAD!

LOOK, I'M TRYIN' TO GET IT, DAWG! CHILL! IT'S JUST A ROCK!

AND IT'LL JUST BE MY FOOT ALL UP IN YO ASS!

WAIT, STOP!
AT LEAST LET ME KEEP MY CREDIT CARDS!
BITCH, I GOT A GUN!
NOW EITHER YOU GIMME THE PURSE OR YOU DIE AND I GET THE PURSE ANYWAY!

BUT THAT'S A BETSEY JOHNSON! IT'S PART OF HER LATEST LINE!

TELL HER I GOT 3 KIDS TO FEED! THAT BANKRUPT CORPSE KNOWS ABOUT HARD TIMES!

HELP!! THIEF!! SOMEBODY CALL THE POLICE!!!

S#!T! TERRIBLE ECONOMY TO LOSE YOUR PURSE IN. A SAFER, MUGGER-LESS ROUTE IS APROPOS. DON'T GET SCARED, MARS.

ONE WAY
The Bard
BEST COAST
THURSDAY, DEC 18
IRON AND WINE
TUESDAY, DEC 30
I GUESS THIS IS A SAFER ROUTE. NO DOPE FIENDS OR MUGGERS HERE. WE'RE GOOD, MARS.

LIKE, I DON'T HAVE ANY F@#!?N' MONEY....

AAAA AHH!

OMIGAWD! TURN IN UP! THAT'S, LIKE, SO MY SONG!
MINE TOO! KREAY'S, LIKE, THE BEST EVER!!

1 • • • 5 • • • 10

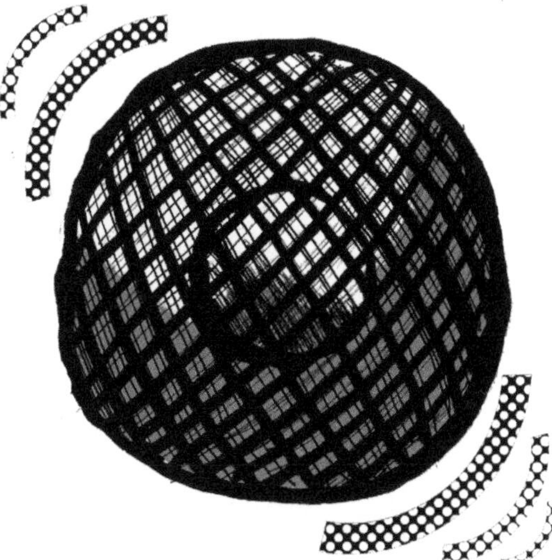

N-N-NO!

HEY BITCH!!!
DO YOU REALLY REALLY REALLY WANNA GO HARD?
LA LA LA LA LA LA LA LA LA
LA LA LA LA
LA LA LA LA
LA LA LA LA LA LA
SHE'S TAKING OVER THE BLOCK! NOW I'M SCARED!!!
T-T-TAXI!!!

BOHEMIAN BOOKS
blackwax boulevard
JOHNSON NEWITT
TAXSERVICE

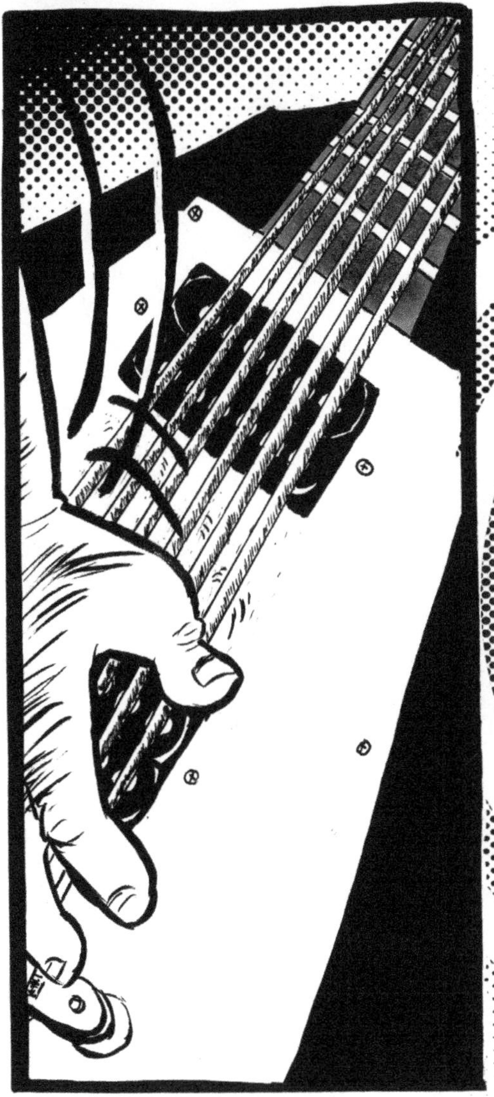

has he
lost his mind?
can he
see
or
is he
blind?

IRON MAIDEN
Marshall
Marshall
PIZZA
PIZZA
PIZZA

THANK YOU GREENVILLE!!!
?#!@!
&#?!?
?#!@!
!&@#?
#$?*!
PIPE DOWN, YA PRICK!!
SHUT UP, ASSWIPE!
UGH! COME ON!
TURN THAT S#!T DOWN!!
ARE YOU F?&@!N' KIDDING ME?!?!

#2

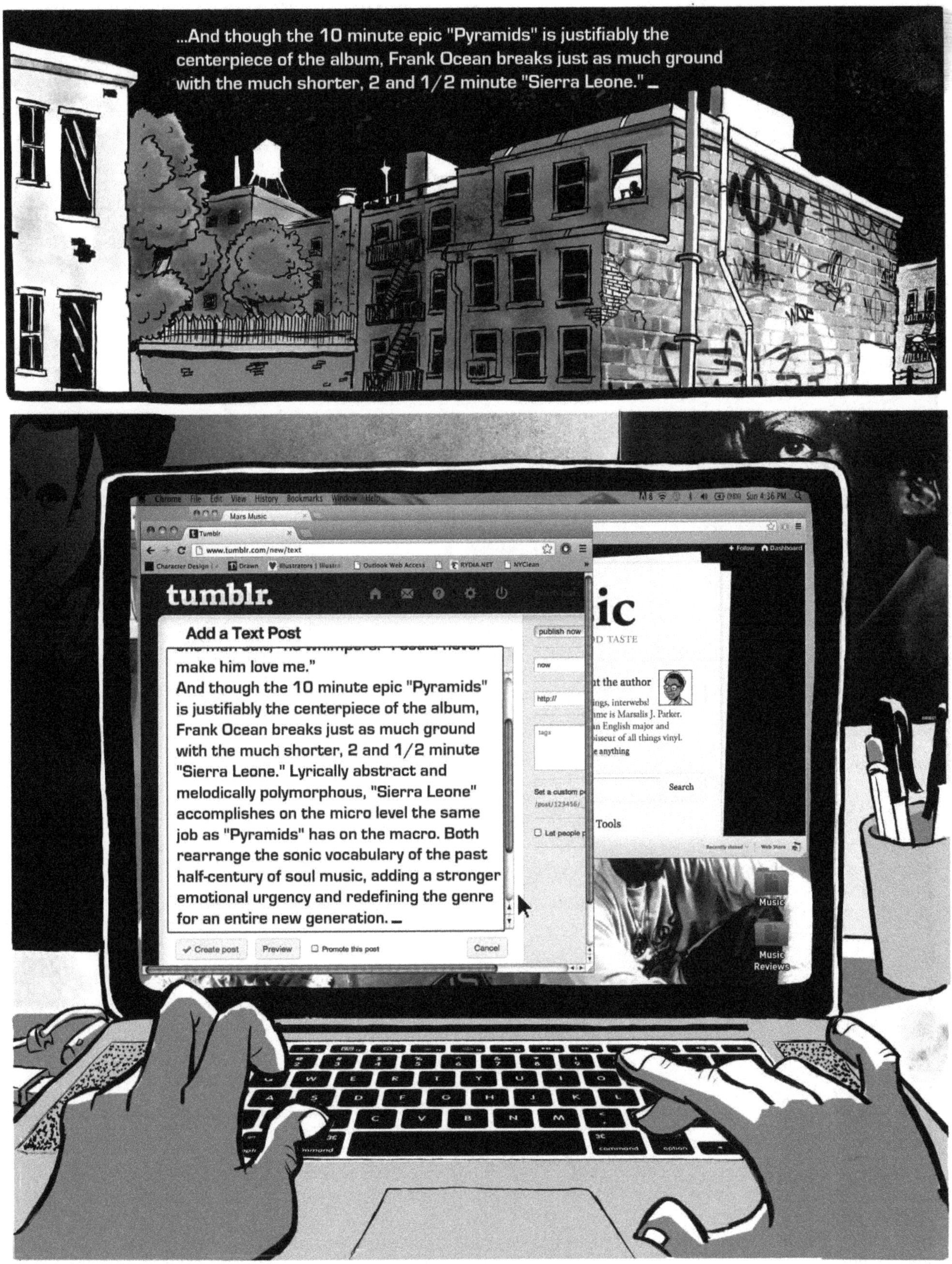

tumblr.

Add a Text Post

make him love me."
And though the 10 minute epic "Pyramids" is justifiably the centerpiece of the album, Frank Ocean breaks just as much ground with the much shorter, 2 and 1/2 minute "Sierra Leone." Lyrically abstract and melodically polymorphous, "Sierra Leone" accomplishes on the micro level the same job as "Pyramids" has on the macro. Both rearrange the sonic vocabulary of the past half-century of soul music, adding a stronger emotional urgency and redefining the genre for an entire new generation. _

Create post | Preview | Promote this post | Cancel

Music

Music Reviews

The assurance and sheer musical force of Channel Orange guarantees it a place on the list of the decade's greatest albums and makes Ocean's recent coming out appear as a mere footnote.
D-D-DONE.

D-D-DAMMIT, I SUCK! WHY DID I EVER M-M-MAJOR IN ENGLISH?!

DELETE POST
BETTER. BETTER. BETTER. BETTER. BETTER.
click

The recent revelation of Frank Ocean's bisexuality was a taboo-shattering moment in urban music, which is fortunately eclipsed by the greatness of his debut album...

WELL, YOU KNOW HER NAME?
I W-W-WISH. ONLY THING I KNOW ABOUT HER IS SHE LIKES THE WHO AND BUYS A LOTTA D-D-DE LA SOUL 45S.

IT'S SO W-W-WEIRD. I SHOULDN'T BE ATTRACTED TO HER, G-G-GIVEN SHE HAS THE EXTERNAL TRAPPINGS OF A COOKIE-CUTTER HIPSTER. BUT HER MUSICAL T-T-TASTES SUGGEST STRONG MENTAL STABILITY AND A SOLID P-P-PROGRESSIVE VALUE SET.
RADIOHEAD
HOW DO YOU KNOW FOR SURE SHE'S A HIPSTER? WHAT IF SHE'S A LEGSTER? OR A FOOTSTER?

WELL, F-F-FOR ONCE, JUST LOOK AT HER OUTFIT:
RASTAFARIAN CAP AND DREADS; ALLUDES TO JAMAICAN CULTURE, POLITICAL CONSCIOUSNESS, EARTHINESS, WEED-SMOKING
OBSCURE BRAZILIAN POP ALBUM; SHOWCASES SELECT TASTE IN MUSIC
RAGGED CAMOUFLAGE JACKET; TRADITIONAL MILITARY ATTIRE ADORNED IRONICALLY TO SUGGEST SOCIOPOLITICAL AWARENESS
RIPPED SHORT SHORTS; EVOKES BIKER CULTURE, REBELLION, DANGER
PIGEON-TOED STANCE; IMPLIES PRECOCIOUSNESS, SEXUAL IMPISHNESS; POPULAR STANCE AMONG FEMALE HIPSTERS
BLACK COTTON LEGGINGS; EMPHASIZES SHAPE OF LEGS, FEMININITY
LEATHER HEELS; PROVIDING FEMININE CONTRAST TO PREDOMINANTLY TOMBOY APPEARANCE

INDEED, SHE WOULD D-D-DO A BK DWELLER VERY PROUD. N-N-NOT SURE, BUT MAYBE HER INDIENESS IS SO INDIE, IT'S QUITE A T-T-TURN ON.
BUT SHE'S A SPLENDID V-V-VESSEL OF INDIE SENSIBILITIES.

I SEE. DOES THAT MEAN PEOPLE AT THE HOMELESS SHELTER ARE INDIE TOO?

WHY ARE YOU SHY? JUST GO ASK HER HER NAME.
SSSSHHHHHH!!! SEUNG-JIN, I C-C-CAN'T JUST WALK UP TO A PRACTICAL S-S-STRANGER AND ASK HER OUT.
TELEVISION

DON'T BE NERVOUS. JUST USE THOSE FANCY, SMART-SOUNDING WORDS YOU USE ALL THE TIME ON YOUR BLOG. SHE'LL LIKE THAT. I DO.

THANKS, KID. B-B-BUT IT'S EASIER SAID THAN DONE. AND EVEN THAT'S N-N-NOT EASY FOR ME. I'M A WRITER. NOT A S-S-SPEAKER.

THEN I'LL SPEAK FOR YOU.
HEY LADY! THIS GUY THINKS YOU'RE TOO INDIE AND WANTS TO ASK YOU OUT!
NO, DON'T!

UH, WHAT GUY? LISTEN, KID, WHOEVER HE IS, WHEREVER HE IS, TELL HIM I'M ALREADY TAKEN.
ZOOM
?

NEVER MIND, MARSALIS! SHE'S ALREADY TAKEN!
G-G-GOOD LOOKING OUT, SEUNG-JIN.

COME ON NOW, VERONIKA. IT'S LUNCHTIME. ONE MEASLY LITTLE SHOT WON'T KILL YA. IT'S ON ME. THINK OF IT AS *CELEBRATING* SOBRIETY, EH? YOU OWE YOURSELF A LITTLE CHEATING, SEXY.
UH, KEEP THE CHANGE, BY THE WAY.
MAIL
pop/rock
THANKS, LEE JIM. BUT FOR THE LAST TIME, I'M *NOT* GOING TO THE BAR WITH YOU OR ANYONE, FOR THAT MATTER.
THIS IS MY *10TH MONTH SOBER* AND I DON'T PLAN ON CHEATING ANYTIME SOON. YOU'LL JUST HAVE TO FIND SOMEONE ELSE.

A LATE NIGHT FULL OF WINE MEANS A LONG MORNING IN THE CONFESSION BOOTH. THAT'S OVER FOR ME. BESIDES, I'M NOT YOUR TYPE ANYWAY.
I'M WAY TOO *LIZ PHAIR, CIRCA 1993,* FOR YOU TO HANDLE.

MAIL
HEY, 1993'S A GOOD YEAR, LIKE A BOTTLE OF WINE. BUT WE CAN GO WHEN I GET DONE WITH WORK, HAVE SOME NON-ALCOHOLIC DRINKS AT *MY* PAD. AND I CAN PLAY YOU THIS DEMI LOVATO RECORD. IT'LL BE *FUN!*

RRRIIIIIIIIIIGGHTT! AND PLAY THAT ALONGSIDE ALL THOSE *SELENA GOMEZ AND HILARY DUFF AND CHEETAH GIRLZ RECORDS* YOU BUY? CALL ME WHEN YOUR RECORD COLLECTION GETS LESS *ROMAN POLANSKI-ISH!*
FREAK OUT!

SO, HOW'S YOUR LOVERBOY DOIN' TODAY?
employees only
KNOCK KNOCK KNOCK
¡AY DIOS MIO! THAT GUY CREEPS ME THE F#@$ OUT! THERE'S ONLY A CERTAIN KIND OF MIDDLE-AGED MAN WHO LISTENS TO TEEN-POP AND CONSIDERS SELENA GOMEZ AS TOO OVER-THE-HILL. WHO KNOWS HOW MANY YOUNG GIRLS HE'S GOT TIED UP IN HIS "BACHELOR PAD"? AND HE HAD THE NERVE TO OFFER ME SHOTS!

WELL, THAT'S AN OBLIVIOUS DOUCHE FOR YA.
GULP GULP

BY THE WAY, WE GOT SOME MORE USED VINYLS COMING IN. SO MAKE SOME ROOM BACK HERE. YOU SHOULD SEE WHAT ONE CHICK BROUGHT IN TODAY. I MEAN, IT'S A TRAVES---

HEY, GET THAT S#!T OUTTA MY FACE! YOU'RE GONNA GIVE ME THE SHAKES AGAIN.
OH F#@$! SORRY!

BUT YOUR SHAKES'LL BE WORSE ONCE YOU SEE WHAT SHE BROUGHT: BEST COAST'S LAST ALBUM.
"THE ONLY PLACE"? I FEEL A SEIZURE COMING ON.

I MEAN, LIKE, THIS IS WHAT MY GAL PAL GOT ME FOR MY BIRTHDAY. SHE DIDN'T KNOW I ALREADY HAD ***THE ONLY PLACE***. SHE JUST KNOWS I LOVE BEST COAST. LIKE, IT'S SO ***RIDIC*** HOW TALENTED THEY ARE.
RADIOHEAD

THEIR FASHION LINE IS SO ***INCRED!*** I MEAN, BETHANY'S, LIKE, SUCH A GENIUS! YOU SHOULD SEE THE LINE SHE MADE FOR ***URBAN***.

ESPECIALLY THE CHER DRESS FROM CLUELESS. ***CLUELESS!*** LIKE, WHO THINKS OF THAT?! AND THIS LIV CROP TOP AND SKIRT ARE SO GORGEOUS, I COULD DIE. SHE'S SO ***F@#?!NG AWESOME!***
BEST COAST

AND HER ***M-M-MUSIC?*** SHE IS A MUSICIAN FIRST, AFTER ALL. GOT ANY TH-TH-THOUGHTS ON HER WRITING? ANY FAVORITE S-S-SONGS?

OH, UH...UH...THE ONE THAT GOES LIKE, UH...HMM... ***THE ONE WHERE SHE'S TALKING ABOUT HER BOYFRIEND.*** THAT'S A GOOD ONE!

YOU M-M-MEAN, **ALL OF THEM.**

THAT'S BULLS#!T! STEVIE'S GOT NOTHING ON MOONDOG.
OH, REALLY?! HOW DO YOU FIGURE THAT?
MOONDOG

LOOK, MOONDOG WAS A REAL ARTIST, OKAY? HE LIVED ON THE STREETS MOST OF HIS LIFE. HE TAUGHT HIMSELF HOW TO WRITE MUSIC AND POETRY. AND HE'S JAZZ, CLASSICAL, AND AVANT-GARDE, ALL IN ONE! YOU CAN'T TOP THAT.
MOONDOG

YAWN! SO WAS MINGUS. PEOPLE KNOW STEVIE MORE. BLIND SINCE BIRTH, UNLIKE M.D. BETTER ALBUMS. BROUGHT TECHNOLOGY TO THE FOREFRONT. NO STEVIE, NO SYNTHS OR R&B AS WE KNOW IT.

OH, YOU AND YOUR TECHNOLOGY. M.D. MADE HIS OWN INSTRUMENTS! AND HE NEVER RECYCLED HIS OWN MUSIC AS HE GOT OLDER.
MOONDOG

BUT HE ONLY HAD TWO GOOD ALBUMS IN HIM, RIGHT? THAT ONE ALBUM NAMED MOONDOG AND THAT OTHER ALBUM NAMED MOONDOG. STEVIE RUNS CIRCLES AROUND HIM IN MAKING RECORDS, MR. ANALOG.

I DISAGREE, THOUGH I WOULD PAY TO SEE ONE BLIND MAN RUNNING AROUND ANOTHER. HOW LONG BEFORE THEY BUMP INTO EACH OTHER?

C'MON, MR. ROLLINS. JUST ONE MORE. PLEASE? IT'S SUPER-GOOD.
LOOK, LITTLEFOOT, HOW MANY QUESTIONS YOU GOT?! I ALREADY TOLD YOU EVERYTHING.
THE DOCTORS CUT MY LEG OFF. I SAID I DIDN'T WANT A FAKE ONE. I FIXED ME A GUITAR INSTEAD.
NOW PLEASE! MR. ROLLINS'S GOT A LOTTA WORK TO DO! THESE SALES AIN'T GONNA REVIEW THEMSELVES!

AND CUE THE SAD PUPPY FACE. DON'T FALL FOR THE SAD PUPPY FACE.........F@#?!N' A!

ALRIGHT, ALRIGHT! ONE MORE QUESTION. BUT IT'D BETTER BE REALLY IMPORTANT.

WHEN YOU LOSE YOUR OTHER LEG TO DYE-UH... DEE-AH-BET--
DIABETES?
YEAH, THAT. WILL YOU PUT A VIOLIN ON IT FOR ME? SO WE CAN JAM?

AH-HAHAHAHA!! SURE, LITTLEFOOT. I'LL MAKE MYSELF A MEMO.

I MEAN, IT'S RID-D-DICULOUS! IF PEOPLE FOLLOW A BLOG AS S-S-STUPID AS CATS THAT LOOK LIKE RON SWANSON, S-S-SURELY THEY COULD FOLLOW MY M-M-MUSIC REVIEWS. IT ACTUALLY HAS PURPOSE, LOGIC, S-S-SUBSTANCE!
SALE!
CLICK
CLICK
CLICK

IT'S BEEN R-R-RUNNING FOR 2 WHOLE MONTHS NOW! AND Z-Z-ZERO FOLLOWERS! MAYBE I'M REVIEWING TOO MANY IR-R-RELEVANT ALBUMS.
CLICK
CLICK
CLICK
CLICK

WELL, YOU'RE ONLY HAVE 2 REVIEWS POSTED. BOTH ARE GREAT THOUGH, LIKE YOUR CHANNEL ORANGE REVIEW. BUT IF YOU WANT FOLLOWERS, YOU GOTTA CRANK OUT THE POSTS.

B-B-BUT THERE'S AN ESOTERIC SCIENCE TO A REVIEW THAT YOU C-C-CAN'T JUST REPLICATE LIKE A BLOG POST. REVIEWS HAVE TO BE P-P-PERFECT.
CLICK
CLICK
CLICK
CLICK
CLICK
CLICK
CLICK
CLICK
CLICK

IF MY REVIEW DOESN'T C-C-CAPTURE THE ESSENCE OF AN ALBUM'S LISTENING EXPERIENCE, W-W-WHAT'S THE USE IN POSTING?
CLICK
CLICK
CLICK
LEONARD COHEN
CLICK
CLICK
CLICK

IT'S JUST A BLOG, MARS. THE MORE YOU POST, THE BETTER YOU'LL GET. I'M SURE CHRISTGAU NEVER STARTED OUT GREAT. YOU DON'T KEEP WRITING, YOU'LL JUST BE AXL ROSE-ING YOUR LIFE AWAY. NOW I'M GONNA PUT OL' LENNY SOMEWHERE YOU CAN'T TOUCH HIM.
SALE!

HEY, IF I'M A PERFECTIONIST, CALL IT B-B-BENNY GOODMAN-ING! AT LEAST HIS M-M-MUSIC HAD PURPOSE AND HE D-D-DIDN'T DATE HACKS LIKE LANA DEL REY!
SALE!
TOMATO, TOMAHTO! JUST WRITE!

OK, GUYS. THEY MAY NOT BE IMACS, MAY NOT EVEN BE I-ANYTHING. BUT THESE ARE THE BEST COMPUTERS WE CAN AFFORD.
AND WE DON'T HAVE TO RELY ON THAT S#!TTY OLD CASH REGISTER ANYMORE. THESE TWO BABIES WILL MAKE FOR FASTER SERVICE AND SHORTER CHECK-OUT LINES.

I M-M-MIGHT HAVE A LOUSY MEMORY, BUT AREN'T OUR L-L-LINES SHORT ANYWAY? INSTEAD OF B-B-BLOWING CASH ON AN ANTIQUE ROADSHOW, YOU COULD'VE GOT SOME M-M-MUSIC THAT ACTUALLY BOOSTS OUR R-R-REPUTATION AGAIN.
pop/rock

AND WHERE EXACTLY DID YOU GET THESE 18TH CENTURY MONITORS? THE GOODWILL?!
SWIPE

YOU MEAN, THE SAME PLACE YOU GOT THOSE F@&#IN' HOOPS IN YOUR EARS? LOOK MAN, THESE COMPUTERS WILL BRING US CLOSER INTO THE 21ST CENTURY. THEY'RE BABY STEPS, BUT STEPS IN THE RIGHT DIRECTION.

AHHH, W-W-WINDOWS MILLENNIUM EDITION AND A FLOPPY DRIVE. THIS M-M-MIGHT BOOST OUR HIPSTER REP AFTER ALL.

SO THAT'S PORKY PIG, EH?
SHHHHH! CHYEAH, BRO. YOU JUST GOTTA HEAR HIM. HE'S F@#&IN' HILARIOUS.

EXCUSE ME, SIR! WE'RE LOOKING FOR THE HIT SINGLE BY THE KNACK, BUT WE FORGOT THE TITLE.
pop/rock

Y-Y-YOU AGAIN?! WHAT DO YOU R-R-R-RETARDS WANT NOW?

HA HA HA HA
HAHA-HA HA
HAHA

LOOK, M-M-MY JOB DESCRIPTION DOESN'T INCLUDE HELPING NEANDERTHALS LIKE Y-Y-YOU! NOW ARE YOU REALLY HERE FOR THE KNACK OR N-N-NOT?
TEE HEE
TEE HEE
HEE HEE

WE'RE SORRY BRO. ACTUALLY, WE'RE REALLY LOOKING FOR A VINYL OF THE WHO. IT'S THEIR FIRST ALBUM FROM '65.
I THINK IT'S, UH, THE WHO SINGS MAGIC BUS?

OH, I THINK YOU'RE TALKING ABOUT MY G-G-GENE---
HAHAHA HA HA HA HA

P-P-PISS. OFF.
HAHA HA HA HA HA HA HA HA HA HA

UH, GUYS. I THINK YOU'RE LOST. **THE DICKWEED CONVENTION** IS THREE BLOCKS DOWN. AND ON YOUR WAY OUT, GIVE THAT MASCARA BACK TO THE **NEW YORK DOLLS** WHERE YA GOT IT!

NEW YORK DOLLS? IS THAT LIKE **PUSSYCAT DOLLS?**

N-N-NEW YORK DOLLS, ONE OF THE MAIN PROGENITORS OF 70S GLAM ROCK. KNOWN FOR THEIR VULGAR ATTITUDE, TRASHY STAGE PRESENCE, AND THEIR PENCHANT FOR M-M-MASCARA.

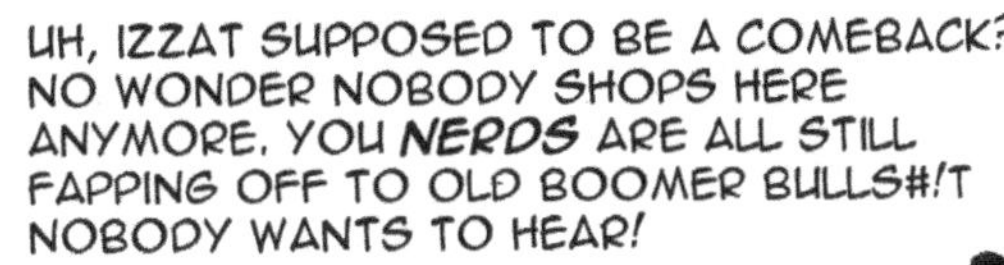
UH, IZZAT SUPPOSED TO BE A COMEBACK? NO WONDER NOBODY SHOPS HERE ANYMORE. YOU **NERDS** ARE ALL STILL FAPPING OFF TO OLD BOOMER BULLS#!T NOBODY WANTS TO HEAR!

PERHAPS, NOBODIES LIKE YOU, ALL CAUGHT UP IN THAT **SKRILLEX CRAP!** BUT FOR KIDS WHO KNOW THE GUESS WHO AIN'T SOME **NEW FRUITY PAIR OF JEANS**, WE'LL ALWAYS BE OPEN!

AARRRGGH! I SEE WE'VE ANGERED **THE HIPPIE PIRATE!**

HA HA HA HA HA HA HA HA HA HA HA HA HA

DEXTER (MARSALIS'S BROTHER)
AH-HAA! THERE Y'ALL MUH'F#?@AS IS! THOUGHT I WOULDN'T FIND YO ASS!

D-D-DEXTER! WHAT THE HELL?!

YEAH, Y'ALL SOME SLICK L'IL NIGGAS RUNNIN' OFF LIKE DAT! AIN'T A MUH'F#$?A IN THE WORLD GET TO LEAVE MY CAB WITHOUT PAYIN' THEY FARE!

EITHER SOMEBODY UP IN HERE PAY DAT $10 NOW, OR G-D AS MY WITNESS...
ONE OF Y'ALL TOSSING MY SALAD!

C-C-COOL IT, BIG BRO! PUT HIM D-D-DOWN! IF ANYBODY, GET THE TALL ONE! HE M-M-MADE FUN OF ME.

OH, REALLY, NOW?

YOU MAKIN FUN A' MY LITTLE BROTHA, HUH? WHAT, YOU GOT A PROBLEM WITH NIGGAS OR SUMTHIN?! DON'T LIKE HIM CUZ HE KNOW MORE ABOUT S#!T THAN YOU?!
DUDE, I DUNNO WHAT YOU'RE TALKING ABOUT! I'M JUST LOOKING FOR SOME MUSIC, 'KAY? PLEASE DON'T CUT ME!

DON'T LISTEN TO THAT L-L-LIAR! HE AND THOSE OTHER JERKS WERE L-L-LAUGHING AT MY S-S-SPEECH PROBLEM!

IZZAT ALL? NIGGA, WHAT ELSE IS NEW? I MAKE FUN A' DAT S#!T ALL THE TIME.
HOW YOU BE TALKIN', HOW YOU BE WALKIN', EVEN HOW YO' POINTY-ASS SHOULDERS BE ON SOME CRAZY LADY GAGA S#!T.

HA HA HA HA HA HEE
HEE HEE HA HA HA HA HEE

BUT I'M HIS MUH'F#?@IN' BROTHA!! I CAN DO DAT S#!T! NOW I WANT MY MONEY!

WHOA-HO-HO! GIVE PEACE A CHANCE, BIG D! HERE, TEN BIG ONES. GO!
classical

NAH, BRUH. DIS NIGGA BOUT PRINCIPLE! I WANT IT FROM HIS POCKET!
AIR...NEED...NOW.

LOOK, DEX, AS MUCH AS I'D LIKE TO WITNESS THE SLAUGHTER OF THESE F#?@S, I GOT A BUSINESS TO RUN, MAN. PUT HIM DOWN.

A'IGHT! FAIR 'NUFF.
WHOOOSH

Y'ALL SOME LUCKY MUH'F#?@AS CUZ MY SALAD WAS GONNA HAVE SOME BIG-ASS CROUTONS UP IN IT!
-COUGH- -COUGH- SALAD?! IS THAT THE BEST THREAT YOU GOT, ASSHOLE?
B-B-BUY THIS INSTEAD AND GO TO TRACK 6. B-B-BEST. THREAT. EVER.
ROCK

"J-J-JELLY OR SYRUP"? HOLY F$&@!
THEY DON'T ACTUALLY DO THAT IN JAIL....RIGHT?
WELL, IF YOU KEEP F$&@ING WITH US, WE CAN CALL THE COPS AND THEY CAN GIVE YOU A TOUR OF THE CITY PENITENTIARY TO FIND OUT. NOW GET, BEFORE I CALL 'EM!
SALE

HEY-HEY! EVEN GOT SOME CRISPY NIGGAS! FRESH OUT DA FACTORY! DAT'S WHAT'S UP!
DEX, AS M-M-MUCH AS I CHERISH "PRINCIPLE", IS IT REALLY WORTH SKYING YOUR B-B-BLOOD PRESSURE OVER TEN BUCKS?

LEMMETELLYA, MARS. THEM NIGGAS IS JUST THE TIP OF THE ICEBERG. ECONOMY GOT E'RYBODY BAILIN' ON CABS. S#!T POPS OFF DAILY. SO I GOTTA GET MINES, BY ANY MEANS NECESSARY.

JUST CURIOUS, MAN. HAVE YOU EVER HAD TO TOSS A SALAD?

HEY MAN, THE ONLY SALAD I EVER TOSS GOTTA BE THICK, DRUNK AND BLONDE, AND WIT A FAT ASS!
SORRY, DUDE. BUT YOU'RE NOT MY TYPE.
!

SAY WHAT?! YOU WANNA RUN THAT BY ME AGAIN? THICK, DRUNK AND BLONDE?!

OR BRUNETTE. I DON'T DISCRIMINATE. ALL THEY NEED IS JUST A JOINT AND SOME PABST IN 'EM, AND THEY ALL PRETTY MUCH FEEL THE SAME ON YOUR MOUTH.

OH, WOW! THAT'S A LOAD OFF MY MIND! YOU ARE THE PINNACLE OF AMERICAN MANHOOD! ALTHOUGH I PITY EVERY POOR THING YOUR MOUTH TOUCHES AFTER YOUR NIGHTLY FREAKERY.
HARDY, I'M BREAKING FOR LUNCH. I FEEL A MIGRAINE COMING ON.

AY, WHAT'S VANESSA'S BEEF? I'M A HARD WORKER OUT IN 'NEM STREETS. CAIN'T A NIGGA GET SOME "RECARATION"? IT BE LONELY OUT THERE DRIVING NIGHTS.
I CAIN'T HELP IT I LIKE A L'IL FREAK ACTION.

ONE, IT'S V-V-VERONIKA. TWO, IT'S "R-R-RECREATION." AND THREE, KEEP THOSE W-W-WATERWORKS AWAY FROM ME!

S#!T, DAT'S RIGHT! I FORGOT. I KNEW HER NAME SOUNDED SEXY, LIKE A DOMINATRIX 'N S#!T. VER-AAHHNN-NEEKUH! SHE NEED A NAME TAG.

MATTA FACT, ALL Y'ALL DO. HOW AM I S'POSED TO KNOW ANY Y'ALL NAMES?
THIS STORE DON'T BELIEVE IN NAME TAGS, MAN.

WE ARE ALL FREE BEINGS HERE. FREE TO BREATH AND FREE TO COEXIST AMONG CRATE-DIGGING BRETHREN. THERE IS NO DIFFERENCE BETWEEN BUYER AND SELLER HERE.
A NAME TAG IS JUST SYSTEMATIZATION OF OUR BEING. TO WEAR ONE IS TO BECOME A COG IN THE CORPORATE MACHINE.

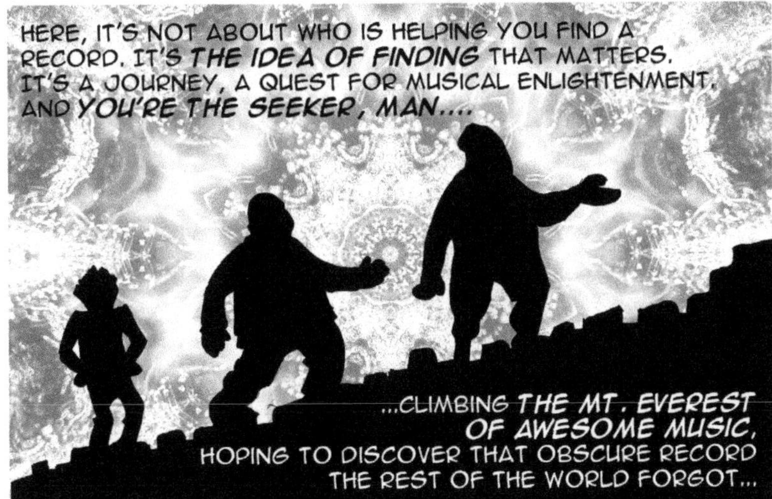
HERE, IT'S NOT ABOUT WHO IS HELPING YOU FIND A RECORD. IT'S THE IDEA OF FINDING THAT MATTERS. IT'S A JOURNEY, A QUEST FOR MUSICAL ENLIGHTENMENT. AND YOU'RE THE SEEKER, MAN....
...CLIMBING THE MT. EVEREST OF AWESOME MUSIC, HOPING TO DISCOVER THAT OBSCURE RECORD THE REST OF THE WORLD FORGOT...

...BEFORE IT GETS OVERUSED IN A MOVIE TRAILER.
Tea for the Tillerman
CAT STEVENS
Hendrix experience
J DILLA JAY DEE DONUTS

AND WE'RE THE GURUS WHO SHOW YOU THE LIGHT... BUT YOU COULD BE THE GURU AND I THE SEEKER! 'CUZ WE'RE ALL ONE! A NAME TAG ONLY DE-EMPHASIZES THE VALUE OF THE SEARCH AND BUILDS UP WALLS BETWEEN OUR BROTHERS AND SISTERS IN VINYL. IT'S JUST ANOTHER FORM OF CORPORATE OWNERSHIP OF ONE'S IDENTITY THAT BLOCKS OUR PATH TO AUDIO NIRVANA.
S-S-SURE, BODHISATTVA. JUST LIKE 3 SHELF FACINGS OF FLO RIDA ARE C-C-CORPORATE OWNERSHIP OF A STORE'S IDENTITY.
SKEEERRCH

F$?#IN' A!
FOR THE LAST TIME, MARS, GET OFF THIS ANTI-DANCE-POP S#!T!

IT'S NOT THE D-D-DANCE-POP, HARDY. IT'S BIGGER THAN THAT. WE WERE GETTING OWNED BY THREE P-P-PISS-ANT KIDS WHO DON'T GIVE A S#!T ABOUT WHAT WE KNOW ABOUT M-M-MUSIC.
WHO DON'T GIVE A S#!T ABOUT "THE SEARCH", THE COMPUTERS WE USE OR THE F-F-FATE OF THE STORE.

AND IF IT WEREN'T FOR "MIKE T-T-TYSON, THE ANGRY YEARS" OVER HERE, I WOULDN'T BE THE ONLY ONE F-F-FACING THE MUSIC....

WE'VE B-B-BECOME DYLAN'S MR. JONES!

DUDE, WATCH THE WAY YOU THROW THAT NAME AROUND! THIS STORE'S COME TOO FAR TO BE IRRELEVANT NOW. YOU CAN'T LET THREE LITTLE F&#?ERS TURN YOUR WORLD UPSIDE DOWN!

WHO THE HELL'S MR. JONES?
C-C-CASE IN POINT.

FIRSTLY, MR. JONES IS A BOURGEOIS SQUARE WITH HIS HEAD UP THE WAZOO, *UNLIKE US.* SECONDLY, HE'S ALWAYS ONE STEP BEHIND EVERYONE AROUND HIM. HE'LL NEVER KNOW WHAT'S IN OR OUT. *AGAIN, UNLIKE US!*
classical
pop/rock

WE'RE STILL HIP TO IT ALL, MAN. WE JUST GOTTA WAIT FOR THE BLIND TO SEE AND APPRECIATE IT AGAIN. AND A LITTLE *DEADMAUS* WON'T HURT WHILE WE WAIT.
'AY!

WHO THE HELL IS THIS GUY? AND WHY HE IN *BLACKFACE?* LOOKS LIKE SOME KINDA *HEAVY METAL MINSTREL MUSIC!*
Lou Reed
METAL MACHINE MUSIC

YOU JUST F-F-FOUND THE STORE'S NEW REPRESENTATIVE. A *L-L-LONG* WAIT TO BEING APPRECIATED.... AS IN *N-N-NEVER.*
ECHH! I SHOULDA BROUGHT 2 PACKS.

OHMYGAWD! THAT'S! EXACTLY WHAT I'VE BEEN LOOKING FOR ALL DAY! THANK YOU! SO! MUCH!
WHAT SHE'S BEEN LOOKING FOR?! SHE SPENDS A GOOD THREE HOURS RUMMAGING THE PLACE, ONLY TO CLAIM AS TREASURE ONE OF THE WORST ALBUMS EVER PRODUCED?!
THIS ISN'T THE MENTALLY STABLE, PROGRESSIVE INTELLECTUAL WHO LOVES DE LA SOUL OR MILTON NASCIMENTO OR THE WHO.... THIS IS JUST ANOTHER UNENLIGHTENED NEANDERTHAL!!!
HYUCK
Lou Reed
MACHINE MUSIC
HYUCK
HYUCK

HOW COULD SHE?!

I THOUGHT I KNEW HER...
OR AT LEAST HER MUSIC-CONSUMING HABITS.

WERE HER PREVIOUS PURCHASES ***JUST A SMOKESCREEN FOR HER TRUE LACK OF TASTE?!***

OR IS SHE ***SO INDIE AND AVANT-GARDE,*** SHE'S LOST HER SENSE OF WHAT GOOD MUSIC IS?
I ***HATE*** NOT KNOWING!

REGARDLESS, SHE CAN'T JUST WALK OUT OF HERE CLUTCHING SUCH ***DRECK!***
THE NUMBER OF UNSUSPECTING VICTIMS POTENTIALLY EXPOSED TO THAT CULTURAL PLAGUE IS UNFATHOMABLE!
NO! SHE MUST BE STOPPED!

UH, IS HE GONNA BE OKAY?

HE A'IGHT. THAT'S JUST HOW HE LOOK WHEN HE THINK TO HIMSELF.

YOU SHOULDA SEEN HIM WHEN A GUY BOUGHT THE NEW BON JOVI ALBUM...... ***PRICE-LESS!***

RADIOHEAD

HARDY, ARE Y-Y-YOU AWARE OF THE HAVOC THAT'LL BE WROUGHT IF WE LET THIS S-S-SIMPLE-MINDED GIRL PROLIFERATE THE HORRORS -***ABSOLUTE HORRORS!***- OF THAT ALBUM?! THE D-D-DAMAGE IS UNIMAGINABLE!

YES, I KNOW! THE MUSIC GODS AGREE! IT'S REED'S WORST! BUT ARE ***YOU*** AWARE OF THE PROFITS WE COULD BE TAKIN' IN WITHOUT YOU ***FREAKIN' OUT*** ABOUT SOMEBODY WITH DIFFERENT TASTE THAN YOURS?! ***I'LL RISK THE APOCALYPSE! NOW, HOP TO!***

'AY MAN, LOOK! YOU JUST GOTTA WORK WITH HIM. I GOTTA LIVE WITH THE MUH'F#@?A!
CHK CHK CHK
OPEN
HE MUST BE LISTENING TO TOO MUCH WEEZER OR SOMETHING. HE'S BEEN GETTING KINDA EMO LATELY.
MAN, I DON'T HARDLY KNOW WHAT HE LISTENIN' TO IN HIS ROOM. IT STAY PACKED WITH ALL KIND A' RECORDS! I CAIN'T EVEN OPEN THE DOOR HALF THE TIME, WITH HIS S#!T IN THE WAY. IT'S EVEN STARTIN' TO TRAVEL INTO THE REST OF MY PAD!
KEEP THE GREEN IN GREENVILLE
TAXI
HA! SOUNDS LIKE HE'S STARTIN' UP HIS OWN STORE.
Y'KNOW, I TELL HIM ALL TH' TIME HE SHOULD SELL SUM'A DEM RECORDS.
BUT, NO, NO! "MY C-C-COLLECTION IS A PERMANENT RECORD OF MY KNOWING WHAT WAS, WHY IT WAS, WHAT WILL BE, BLAH, BLAH, BLAH." ON DAT DEEP THINKER S#!T.
AND ALL DAT WRITIN' HE DO, WHY CAIN'T HE WRITE UP HIS SHARE OF THE MUH'F#@?IN' RENT?!
WELL, DON'T COME BUSTIN' MY DOOR DOWN FOR ANOTHER BAILOUT. HE'LL BE JUST A DEAD F#@?ER.
SLIPSTREAM BOOKS

YOU KNOW, TH-TH-THIS CD IS JUST FOR DISPLAY. THERE'S N-N-NOTHING INSIDE THE CASE. SO I'M AFRAID I CAN'T HELP YOU.
HMM...STRANGE. FELT PRETTY WEIGHTY TO ME. EVEN THE WRAPPING LOOKS NEW.

WELL, S-S-SOMETIMES THE SHIPMENTS WE GET COME WITH SOME MESSED-UP UNITS. NOTHING IN IT, BUT THE M-M-MACHINES WRAP THEM UP ANYWAY. I WAS J-J-JUST ABOUT TO THROW IT OUT.

OH NO THAT'S! OKAY. I'LL TAKE IT OFF YOUR HANDS FOR FREE, THEN. I COULD USE A NEW DRINK COASTER. LESS TRASH FOR THE OZONE LAYER TO DEAL WITH.

UH, B-B-BUT IT HAS TO BE COUNTED FOR INVENTORY CLAIMS. SO IT'S STILL KINDA OURS. UM, IF YOU'RE STILL L-L-LOOKING FOR SOMETHING AVANT-GARDE, THE JAZZ SECTION JUST G-G-GOT SOME NEW STUFF BY JOHN ZORN.

BUT YOU WON'T HAVE TO WORRY ABOUT COUNTING IT AS A DAMAGE CLAIM IF I STILL WANNA BUY IT. BESIDES, IRONICALLY OWNING BAD MUSIC IS PERFECT FOR A "COOKIE-CUTTER HIPSTER."
ISN'T IT, MARSALIS?

Y-Y-YOU....KNOW MY N--
CD. NOW!

FYI, THIS ISN'T FOR RECREATION. IT'S FOR A ***PERFORMANCE PIECE*** I'M DOING.
RADIOHEAD
RAM

P-P-PERFORMANCE? YOU A M-M-MUSICIAN?

MM-MMM. DANCER. ***MODERN*** DANCER, MIND YOU. MY CLOTHES ALWAYS STAY ***ON***. I'M PART OF A GROUP HERE IN THE CITY. YOU KNOW THE ***GREENVILLE GLISSÉS?***

GREENVILLE G-G-GLISSÉS?

OH YEAH! HEY, YOU MUST BE A G-G-GOOD DANCER. ***THAT'S THE CITY'S P-P-PREMIER DANCE COMPANY.***

WELL, I ***ASPIRE*** TO BE GOOD. HEHEHE. BUT IT'S NOW THE CITY'S ***ONLY*** DANCE COMPANY. THE OTHERS SHUT DOWN YEARS AGO.

AH, THE P-P-PERILS OF BEING A NON-PROFIT. SO WHAT'S THE P-P-PERFORMANCE PIECE ABOUT? ***HOW MUCH LOU REED SUCKS WHEN HE'S ON T-T-TOO MUCH GRASS?***
HE DOES SOUND BETTER ON ***HEROIN*** THAN GRASS, DOESN'T HE?

AND THIS BABY CAN RETRACT, EXTEND, TWIST AROUND. CAN EVEN SWAP OUT A DIFFERENT AXE IF I WANTED.

DAMN! DIDN'T KNOW THEY COULD MAKE SMALL V'S LIKE DIS.

THEY CAN'T. ***I CAN THOUGH.*** MY UNCLE JIMMY TAUGHT ME HOW TO CARVE AN AXE WHEN I WAS YOUNG. HE COULD MAKE ANY KIND. AXES WITH LONG NECKS, SHORT NECKS. BIG FRETS, SMALL FRETS. EVEN CUSTOM BODIES TOO.

SOUND LIKE A GOOD BID'NESS TO ME.

WELL, HE USED TO RUN A LITTLE GUITAR FACTORY IN HIS OWN LIVING ROOM. BUT AFTER FIGHTING IN KOREA, HE DIDN'T WANNA LIFT ONE MORE FINGER DOING MANUAL LABOR.

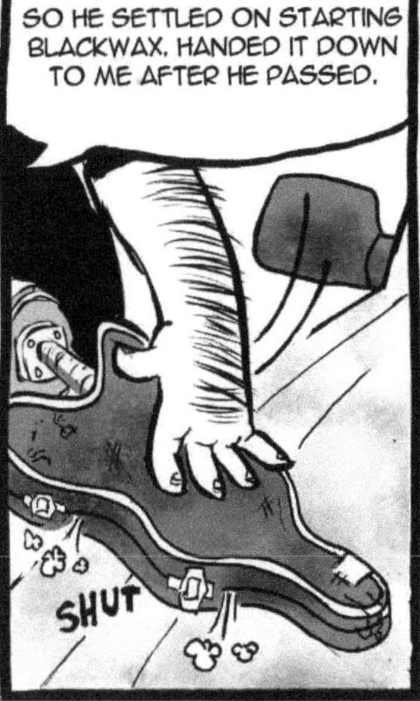

SO HE SETTLED ON STARTING BLACKWAX. HANDED IT DOWN TO ME AFTER HE PASSED.
SHUT

I'LL HAND YOU DOWN *MR. PAY-NO-RENT* WHEN I PASS AWAY.
NAH, I'M GOOD. I'M LOSIN' ENOUGH MONEY *NOW.*

AARRGH! FOR F@#$'S SAKE!
PROBLEM, DARLIN'?
MY LIGHTER'S TOO LOW. YOU GOT ONE ON YOU?
CHK CHK! CHK CHK CHK CHK

SORRY, KID. I LOST MINE A WHILE BACK.
NO WORRIES, BABY. I GOTCHA RIGHT 'CHERE!
DON'T CALL ME "BABY," SALAD MAN.

IF SHE AIN'T DRINKIN', SHE'S SMOKIN'.
YOU STILL GOING TO THOSE MEETINGS?
CHK

ECCHH! WHAT'S THE POINT? IT'S THE SAME, DUMB F#@!ERS TELLING THE SAME, DUMB STORY....

"OH, I HAVEN'T BEEN DRUNK FOR A MONTH! I'M CLEAN! I'M CLEAN! NEVER MIND THE FACT I DO A LINE A DAY TO KEEP ME STRONG."

WELL, YOU'VE BEEN CLEAN FOR ALMOST A YEAR. TELL 'EM YOUR STORY. WHO THE HELL KNOWS? YOU MIGHT COULD BE "INSPIRING."

EH, I COULD. BUT FOR NOW, I'M "INHALING."

MAN, WHAT IS DAT THING ON YOUR ARM, BY THE WAY? SOME KINDA LEAFY S#!T?

NOT QUITE. SUPPOSED TO BE BARBED WIRE. BUT THE GUY INKING WAS TOO HIGH TO DO IT RIGHT. I GOTTA GET IT COVERED UP.

YO, I ALWAYS WANTED A TAT LIKE DAT. SUMTHIN' TOUGH-LOOKIN'. S#!T DAT LOOK LIKE IT'S SWOOPIN' AROUND ON MY CHISELED FRAME.

WELL, RONNIE COLEMAN, IT'S VERY EASY TO MAKE. I COULD HOOK YOU UP.
YOU A TATTOO ARTIST?

MMM, ASPIRING TATTOO ARTIST. HAVEN'T DONE IT IN A WHILE AFTER GETTING OFF THE BOTTLE. NOW I SEE WHY YOU SHOULDN'T INK WHILE LOADED. I DO ALRIGHT THOUGH. I CAN'T GET ENOUGH WILLING SUBJECTS TO PRACTICE ON.

AY, I'M 'BOUT IT. HOW MUCH YOU USUALLY CHARGE FOR A TAT LIKE DAT?
ONLY $300.

OH F#@? NO!! I MIGHT LOOK TOUGH, BUT MY WALLET SURE DON'T!

JEEZ, DUDE! I DON'T THINK CHINA HEARD YOU LOUD ENOUGH!
HARDY'LL HAVE TO BE YOUR GUINEA PIG. HIS SKIN'S A LITTLE BLANK FOR A METALHEAD.
HE COULD GO UNDER THE NEEDLE A FEW TIMES.
EXACTLY, RIGHT? LIKE, ONE LITTLE STAR LIKE RIGHT HERE WOULDN'T KILL HIM.
OR MAYBE A DRAGON WITH OPEN WINGS ON HIS BACK? WHAT'S MORE HEAVY METAL THAN THAT?
YEAH! DAT'S WHAT'S UP!
OOH, DAT'S HOT!

WHOA! HEY! I DIG THE CREATIVE STUFF, BUT I'M GOOD, GUYS!
I'VE SEEN ENOUGH NEEDLES FOR A THOUSAND HEADBANGERS!

DAMMIT! I FORGOT TO CHECK MY BLOOD SUGAR TODAY.

YO, MAN...HE BUGGIN' OUT HARD OVER SOME NEEDLES.
7 1 6
SHHH. THAT'S HOW HE GETS WHEN YOU TALK ABOUT THAT STUFF TOO MUCH. JUST LIKE A BABY.
CAN'T EVEN TALK ABOUT TEMPORARY TATS.

THAT'S A CHILD DIABETIC FOR YOU.
OR MAYBE A CHEAPSKATE. IT TAKES ONE TO KNOW ONE.

REALLY, NOW? THAT'S SO UNFAIR.
B-B-BOWIE WASN'T NEEDED.
BUT, BOWIE HELPED GIVE LOU THE RIGHT CONTEXT FOR FAME IN GLAM.

EH, M-M-MAYBE. BUT, BOWIE GOT M-M-MOST OF HIS LYRICAL GAZE FROM LOU.

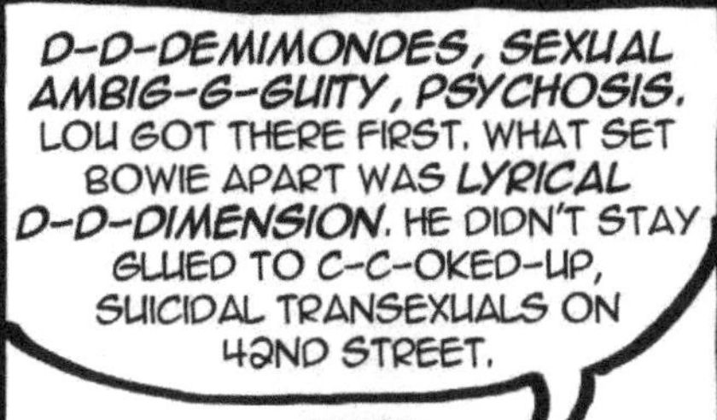
D-D-DEMIMONDES, SEXUAL AMBIG-G-GUITY, PSYCHOSIS. LOU GOT THERE FIRST. WHAT SET BOWIE APART WAS LYRICAL D-D-DIMENSION. HE DIDN'T STAY GLUED TO C-C-OKED-UP, SUICIDAL TRANSEXUALS ON 42ND STREET.

WHAT'S GOING ON HERE?! HE IS HELPING YOU, RIGHT, MA'AM?

SIR, I REALLY MUST SAY THAT YOU HAVE EMPLOYED A RATHER EXQUISITE MUSIC CONNOISSEUR. A MAN OF PROFOUND KNOWLEDGE OF SONG.
NOT ONLY HAS HE HELPED. HE HAS ENLIGHTENED.

classical
I AM A HAPPY, HAPPY, HAPPY CUSTOMER!
INDEED. YOU CAN TH-TH-THANK ME WITH A BONUS LATER.

MAYBE A BONUS LATER. *MUCH* LATER. RIGHT NOW, I GOTTA FIND MY TEST THINGY.

ANYWAY, WE'RE STILL KICKING STUFF AROUND. AND I'M ALSO THE MUSIC SUPERVISOR.

BUT WE WANT THE PERFORMANCE'S THEME TO BE ABOUT *HUMAN CONNECTION*. ABOUT COMMUNICATION. ABOUT ENGAGING WITH THE WORLD AROUND US. ENGAGEMENT OF MIND, SOUL, BODY.

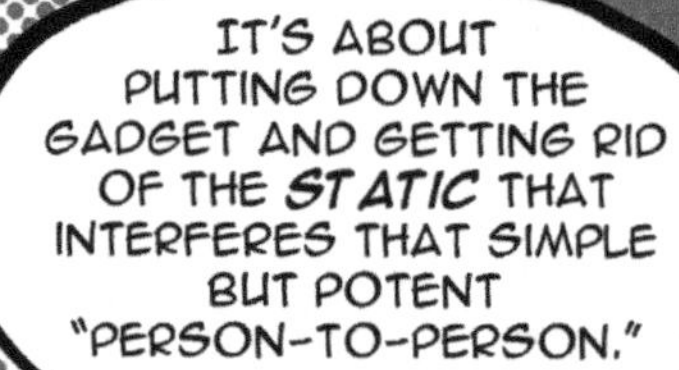
IT'S ABOUT PUTTING DOWN THE GADGET AND GETTING RID OF THE *STATIC* THAT INTERFERES THAT SIMPLE BUT POTENT "PERSON-TO-PERSON."

AND C-C-CUE MR. REED!

BINGO! AND I ONLY NEED A FEW SECONDS OF...WELL...*ANY* SONG ON THE RECORD. BUT I STILL GOTTA TRACK DOWN SOME OTHER MUSIC FOR THE PIECE.

W-W-WAIT. YOU COULD JUST HOP ON *G-G-GOOGLE* AND FIND IT FOR F-F-FREE. WHY B-B-BOTHER DIGGING AROUND HERE?

NO STATIC.

716
YOU KNOW W-W-WHAT'S INTERESTING? REED WAS GIVEN ELECTROSHOCK TH-THERAPY WHEN HE WAS A TEEN TO "C-CURE" HIS BISEXUALITY.
SO ONE COULD FRAME THE ALBUM AS A S-S-SUBCONSCIOUS HEALING PROCESS FOR HIM. THAT'S ONE POSSIBLE LAYER OF M-M-MEANING, ALBEIT VERY THIN.
WOW! I NEVER. THOUGHT OF THAT.
PULP FICTION

YOU SHOULD BE A WRITER FOR PITCHFORK OR SOMETHING. THEY COULD USE A HISTORICALLY MINDED...MIND LIKE YOURS.

W-WELL, I'M ALREADY A WRITER. ASPIRING, THAT'S IT. I DO HAVE A B-BLOG, THOUGH.
YEAH? DETAILS, DETAILS!
IT'S, UH, C-C-CALLED MARS MUSIC. IT'S ON T-T-TUMBLR.
SO IT'S "MARSMUSIC," ONE WORD. DOT TUMBLR, ETC?

SWEET! I'LL CHECK IT OUT ONCE I GET HOME.
N-NO NEED TO RUSH. THE BLOG'S KINDA C-C-CRAPPY AND I DON'T HAVE M-MUCH ON IT.

BUT WHEN YAHOO GETS DONE WITH IT, THE TUMBLRVERSE AT LARGE WILL BE A WHOLE LOT CRAPPIER. I WANNA EXPERIENCE YOUR DIGITAL WISDOM IN ITS PRIME.

W-WELL, I'VE BEEN COMPILING NOTES FOR MY N-N-NEXT ALBUM REVIEW. IT'LL BE ON "THIS IS M-M-MADNESS," BY THE LAST POETS.
GET! OUT! THAT'S MY BOYFRIEND'S FAVORITE ALBUM!
TAX
1

HE LIVES. AND BREATHES! THE LAST POETS. IT'S ALL HE EVER TALKS ABOUT WHEN COMES TO MUSIC. THAT AND PUBLIC ENEMY. HEHEHE.

DAMMIT! THAT'S RIGHT. SHE'S "ALREADY TAKEN."

AH, WELL, HE'S GOT GOOD TASTE. VERY P-P-POWERFUL RECORD. UH, THANKS FOR STOPPING BY. L-L-LATER.

WAIT! DON'T GO! THAT REMINDS ME...

...I ALMOST FORGOT... HE'D KILL ME IF I DIDN'T DO THIS...

WE'RE PROTESTING THE SHUTTERED PUBLIC SCHOOLS AT CITY HALL. THAT'S HIM!

DEMONSTRATION AGAINST THE GREENVILLE PUBLIC SCHOOL CLOSURES
ASSEMBLE AT CITY HALL NEXT MONDAY 1000 AM
LEADING AND SPEAKING AT THE RALLY:
BROTHER RAGE
NEIGHBORHOOD ACTIVIST
savegreenvilleschools.org
SEE THE SCHEMES. SAVE THE SCHOOLS.

YOU KNOW, I TOLD HIM I THOUGHT. MAYBE. JUST MAYBE. PEOPLE WON'T GET IT'S A PROTEST BECAUSE HIS FACE AND NAME TAKES UP MOST OF THE FLYER.

BUT HE TOLD ME, THOUGH, YOU HAVE TO TIE A KNOWN FACE TO AN UNDERGROUND CAUSE. SO I DIDN'T BOTHER HIM ANYMORE.

ANYWAY, HE NEEDS AS MANY ENGAGED, YOUNG MINDS AS POSSIBLE THERE. BE AWESOME AND JOIN US, EH?

LATER, FRIEND!!!

HEY, NOTTA BAD-LOOKIN' **REDBONE**, LIL BRUH! I BET DAT IS **SWEEEET**! YA GET HER NUMBER?

H-H-HOW COULD SHE POSSIBLY SEE VIABLE BOYFRIEND M-M-MATERIAL IN SUCH A **GLIB, POMPOUS, AESTHETICALLY ANTEDILUVIAN C-C-CRANK?!**

HA! I HAD DA SAME QUESTION. CAIN'T FIGURE OUT MOST A' THESE MODERN CHICKS MYSELF, MAN. BUT DON'T WASTE TIME TRYIN'. LIFE'S TOO SHORT FOR DAT.

AND E'RYBODY DESERVES TO HAVE AT LEAST ONE GIRL BEFORE THEY DIE, ANYWAY. **'SPECIALLY YOU.** SO IF SHE FEELIN' YOU, EVEN WITH ALL YO' QUIRKS AND S#!T, LET HER. SHE MIGHT BE DA ONE.

NO, FOOL! ***I M-M-MEANT THIS GUY!***

HMM. WELL, HOMEGIRL DODGED A **HUGE-ASS BULLET**, THEN!
TAXI! LIKE, **HELLO?!**
TAXI

WELL, KEEP YA HEAD UP, BABY BRO. YOU'LL FIND A COOCHIE THAT FITS SOON ENOUGH. NOW I GOT MONEY TO MAKE.
TAXI

ALRIGHT, ALRIGHT, AL-RIIIIIGHT! I'M HERE, PRETTY MAMA. WHERE TO?
5TH AND PERKINS. AND, LIKE, HURRY! I GOT A THING TO GET TO OR I'M GONNA BE LATE!
Ignoring it won't make it better. Seeing a doctor will.
WELL, SIT TIGHT, BABY. BIG D GOTCHOO! JUST SIT YA SLENDA SELF INSIDE AND YOU-
WHAT TH--
TAXI
AH, F$#! DAT! I AIN'T EVEN GONE DAT LONG AND THEY START BOOTIN' NIGGAS!
SO M-M-MUCH FOR LOW BLOOD PRESSURE.

C-C-CRAP! I WAS BORN AWESOME!
WHOA, SPAZ ALERT!

THAT'S WHAT I SH-SHOULD'VE SAID BACK TO HER. "BE AWESOME AND J-J-JOIN US?" "WELL, I WAS BORN AWESOME." THEN, ALL CH-CHANCES FOR AWKWARD SILENCE WOULD'VE BEEN ELIMINATED. I HATE HAVING THE P-P-PERFECT, WITTY RESPONSE ONLY AFTER THE MOMENT PASSES.

WOW. YOU ARE F#@$ING SPRUNG FOR THIS GIRL. THAT'S THE ONLY TIME SOMEONE WORRIES ABOUT WHAT THEY SAY TO THE PERSON THEY LIKE.

L-L-LESS SPRUNG, MORE SQUASHED. SHE HAS A GUY ALREADY. SOME P-P-POLITICO.
BROTHER RAGE

WELL, AT LEAST THAT WHOLE "RASTAFARIAN RADICAL" LOOK MAKES SENSE NOW.
ARE YOU GOING?
S-SNOWBALL'S CHANCE. I'M NO RADICAL....AND I D-DON'T THINK SHE'S ONE EITHER DEEP DOWN. SOMETHING'S N-NOT RIGHT HERE.
HER NAME'S SALIMAH.

SHE'S ONLY A YEAR YOUNGER THAN M-ME, BUT JUST A JUNIOR IN COLLEGE. SHE'S INTO PERFORMING ARTS, ABSTRACT M-M-MODERN DANCE KIND OF STUFF. SEEMS TO POSSESS THE SPARK OF INDIVIDUALITY UNDERNEATH HER S-STEREOTYPICALLY RADICAL ATTIRE....
...WHICH IMPLIES THAT ***HE'S*** F-FASHIONING HER IN HIS IMAGE. THEY LOOK LIKE THEY B-BELONG IN DIFFERENT UNIVERSES. SHE APPEARS REAL EARTHY AND WARM. NONE OF THE PISS, FIRE OR C-C-COCKSURENESS HE POSSESSES.
IT'S USUALLY TYPES L-L-LIKE HIM TO TAKE ADVANTAGE OF GIRLS L-L-LIKE HER, STILL IMPRESSIONABLE WITH A FLUID P-PERSONAL IDENTITY, BEREFT OF THE INTELLECTUAL R-R-RIGOR DEMANDED BY COLLEGIATE AND POST-COLLEGIATE LIFE.
OH YEAH, WE ALL KNOW THOSE COLLEGE YEARS ARE MAKE OR BREAK, RIGHT? BECAUSE ***EVERY*** IMPORTANT THING YOU NEED TO KNOW ABOUT LIFE ONLY EVER HAPPENS IN YOUR DORM. HELL, WHO NEEDS A ***LIFETIME*** OF DIFFERENT EXPERIENCES TO LEARN FROM? ***ALMIGHTY COLLEGE WILL WISE US ALL UP!***
I KNEW YOU'D SEE IT M-M-MY WAY.

MARS, DON'T YOU EVER THINK MAYBE SHE LIKES HIM BECAUSE THEY JUST - I DON'T KNOW - HAPPEN TO SHARE THE SAME PASSIONS IN LIFE? IT IS POSSIBLE FOR HER TO HAVE A MIND OF HER OWN.
C-C-CAN SHE? WHO REALLY HAS A M-M-MIND OF THEIR OWN THESE DAYS?
ONE LOVE
BOB MARLEY

WHY WON'T YOU FIND OUT, THEN? AND NOT BY SEEING WHAT RECORDS SHE BUYS OR WHAT CLOTHES SHE WEARS, BUT JUST SEEING HER.

I ADM-M-MIRE YOUR WISDOM, BUT I GAVE UP ON THAT CONCEIT LONG AGO.
SLIDE

P-P-PEOPLE ONLY LET YOU SEE WHAT THEY WANT YOU TO SEE. THEY CAN H-HIDE PART OF THEMSELVES BEHIND THINGS. CLOTHES, FRIENDSHIPS, POLITICS, YOU N-N-NAME IT.
...BUT THEY CAN'T H-HIDE BEHIND THEIR RECORDS. THEY CAN SPEAK VOLUMES ABOUT P-PEOPLE.... WHERE THEY ARE IN LIFE, WHO THEY ARE, WHO THEY W-WERE AND WHO THEY'LL B-BE. HARD TO BELIEVE, BUT IT'S TRUE. IT'S MY ONLY WAY TO S-S-SEE. OR WAS.

I KNOW A GUY WHO LOVED ALL THE RIGHT RECORDS. THE RONETTES, THE BEATLES, THE RAMONES, JUST TO NAME A FEW.... **HIS NAME IS PHIL SPECTOR.**
MINGUS
THE BLACK SAINT AND THE SINNER LADY
coo ka choo

WE ALL KNOW HOW **HE** TURNED OUT.

GET UN-SQUASHED, SWEETIE.
716
ONE LOVE
BOB MARLEY

OPEN
716
KACHOOM

#3

The affliction of today's skinny-jean loners: too many fingerprints on their imaginations.
They are the guilty victims in man's longest-running game of cultural pickpocketing,
an heirloom of high abstraction, passed from last year's model to this year's model.
Chasing the new. Chasing the old. Chasing the tail.
Pure, unpredjudiced fact. Don't think so?_
♫ ...IT'S A GOD-AWFUL SMALL AFFAIR... ...TO THE GIRL WITH THE MOUSEY HAIR... ♫
BEASTIE BOYS

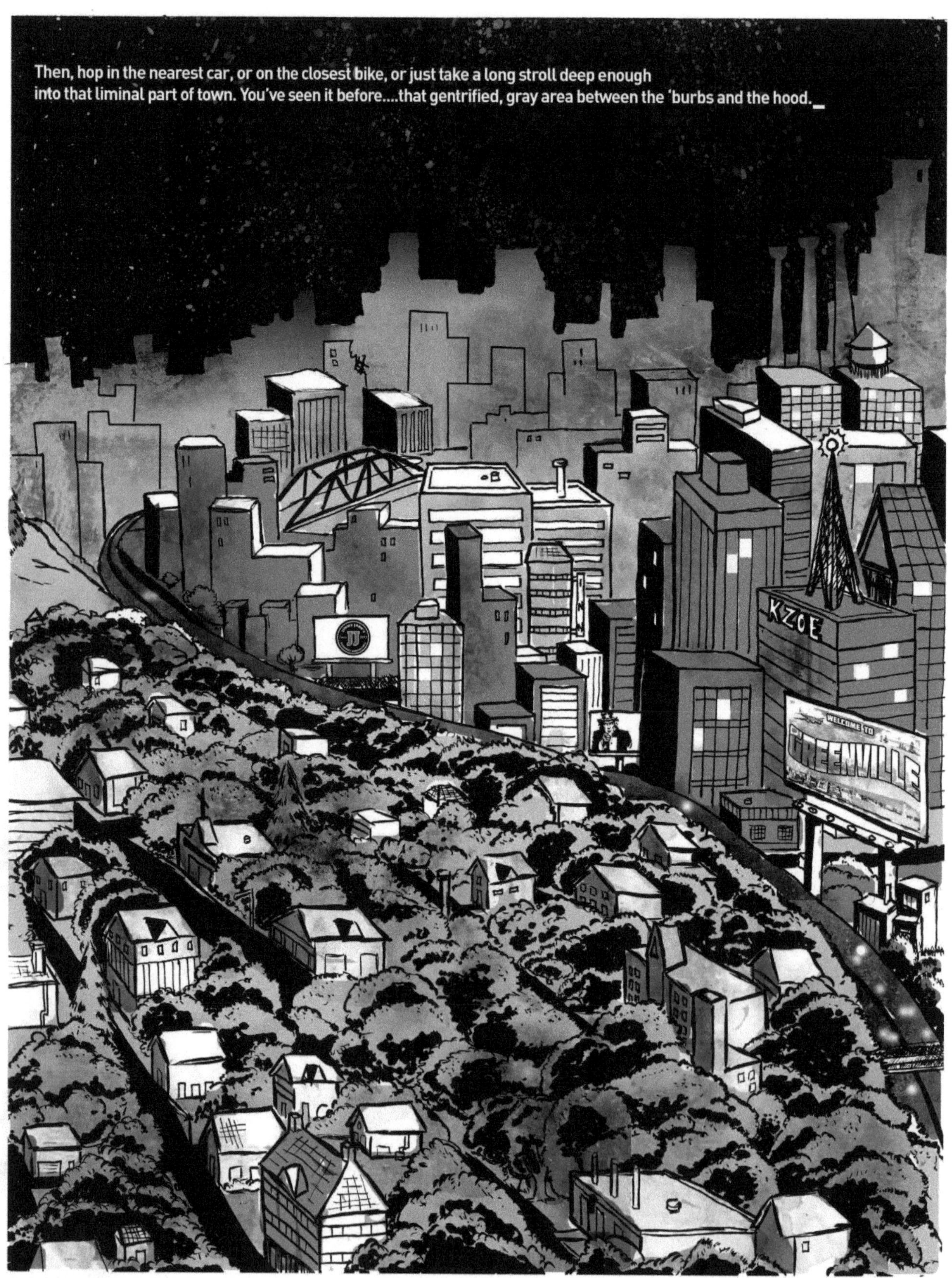
Then, hop in the nearest car, or on the closest bike, or just take a long stroll deep enough into that liminal part of town. You've seen it before....that gentrified, gray area between the 'burbs and the hood._
KZOE
WELCOME TO
GREENVILLE

The Bard

TONIGHT!
MGMT
SOLD OUT

And see an infinite scroll of **Kerouacs and Coltranes and Cobains,** flaunting their new discovery of Wayfarers, Afro-pop and handlebar mustaches. All dying to write, sing, experience or simply **BE** the Next Great Whatever.

ENTER

Trafficking in the **meta-meta-meta**, an insidious exchange of ghostwritten memes and hand-me-down souvenirs from an earlier tastemaker's bout of aesthetic kleptomania.

SURE, CRITICS SAY THE BAND'S NEW STUFF IS GARBAGE. SAID THE SAME THING TO THE VELVET UNDERGROUND.
UMM, DIFFERENT LEAGUES. MGMT EMPHASIZE THE STUDIO MORE. THEY'RE SIMILAR TO BRIAN WILSON, BUT WITH MORE INDISCRIMINATE POP MELODIES.
LOOK, I'M ALL FOR MUSICAL GROWTH AND WHAT NOT, BUT WOULD IT KILL THEM TO, LIKE, PLAY "KIDS" JUST ONCE? NOT EVERYONE DIGS THIS NEW EXPERIMENTAL CRAP.
I LIKE THEIR NEW STUFF, ACTUALLY. IT'S SOMETHING NOBODY'S EVER DONE BEFORE, NOT SINCE THE FLAMING LIPS.
NOBODY!
BULLS#!T!! BEN AND ANDREW ARE THE ONLY DWEEBS FROM WESLEYAN TO MAKE IT IN MUSIC! WESLEYAN'S GOT NOTHING ON UC BERKELEY! WE PRODUCE BIGGER ARTISTS ON OUR CAMPUS!
RIGHT. YOU MEAN LIKE THAT LEAD SINGER FROM THIRD EYE BLIND? OR THAT SHORT CHICK FROM THE BANGLES? OR MAYBE YOU MEAN LIL B?
I WONDER IF THEY DO LSD BACKSTAGE BEFORE THEY PLAY LIKE JIMI HENDRIX DID. MAN, I WISH I WERE A ROADIE IN THE '60S!
NAH, LSD'S NOT COOL CUZ TOO MANY OLD PEOPLE DID IT THEN AND GOT F&#@ED UP. IT'S PROBABLY MOLLY. NOW THAT'S A GLAMOUR DRUG! LIKE, WHO CAN REALLY DIE FROM TAKING TOO MUCH?
KEEP CALM AND NOM NOM

zZzZTTT

BIG

BIG

YEARS AGO, MY HEART WAS SET TO LIVE.....OHHH
The '60s got it wrong. Maybe what it actually witnessed was **the dawning of the Age of Readymades.** Somewhere in the ether, Duchamp is weeping.

Or, at the very least, he suffers from motion sickness, watching us run around and around in frantic pursuit of that Special New Thing on the scene.
GOOD GRIEF! WHERE ARE YOU, YA LITTLE F#@&ER?!

THEY MAKE THESE MONITORS TOO DAMN SMALL NOWADAYS!

BALL SACKS!
CLANK
CLANK

BALL SACKS!

BALL SACKS!
BALL SACKS!!
BALL SACKS!!!
BA--
POOMF
WHOA!
SIMMER, OLD MAN.
JUST LAY OFF THE
SWEETS TONIGHT.
IRON MAIDEN

How did the kids get here? Underneath the flower headbands and chinos, they're just small children, foundlings with the innate desire to grasp for whatever mimics the warm, motherly embrace of the New and Authentic.

Desperately seeking a trustworthy compass to help them navigate through modern life's plastic jungle of bar codes and pop-up ads, white collars and cubicles, lip-synchers and great pretenders.
♫ THAT SILENT SENSE OF CONTENT... THAT EVERYONE GETS... ♫

♫ ...JUST DISAPPEARS... ♫
SNAP SNAP
SNAP
SNAP SNAP

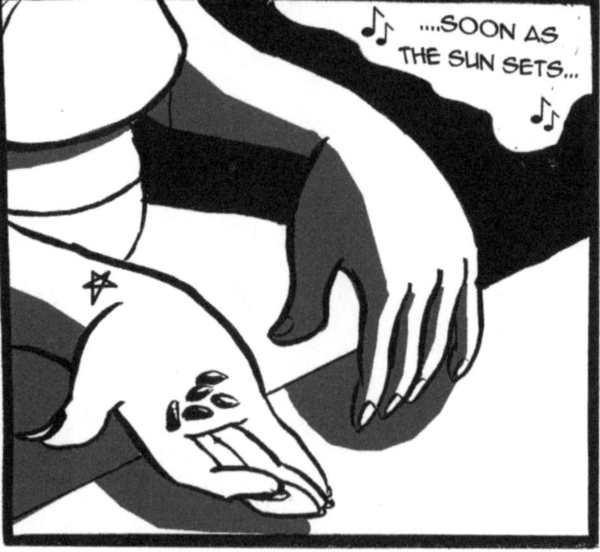
♫ ....SOON AS THE SUN SETS... ♫

THIS FACE IN MY DREAMS SEIZES MY GUTS... HE FLOODS ME WITH DREAD...
SOAKED IN SOUL... HE SWIMS IN MY EYES BY THE BED...
POUR MYSELF OVER HIM...
MOON SPILLING IN...
SEE YOU IN THE MORNING, DUSTY CITY.
AND I WAKE UP ALONE...

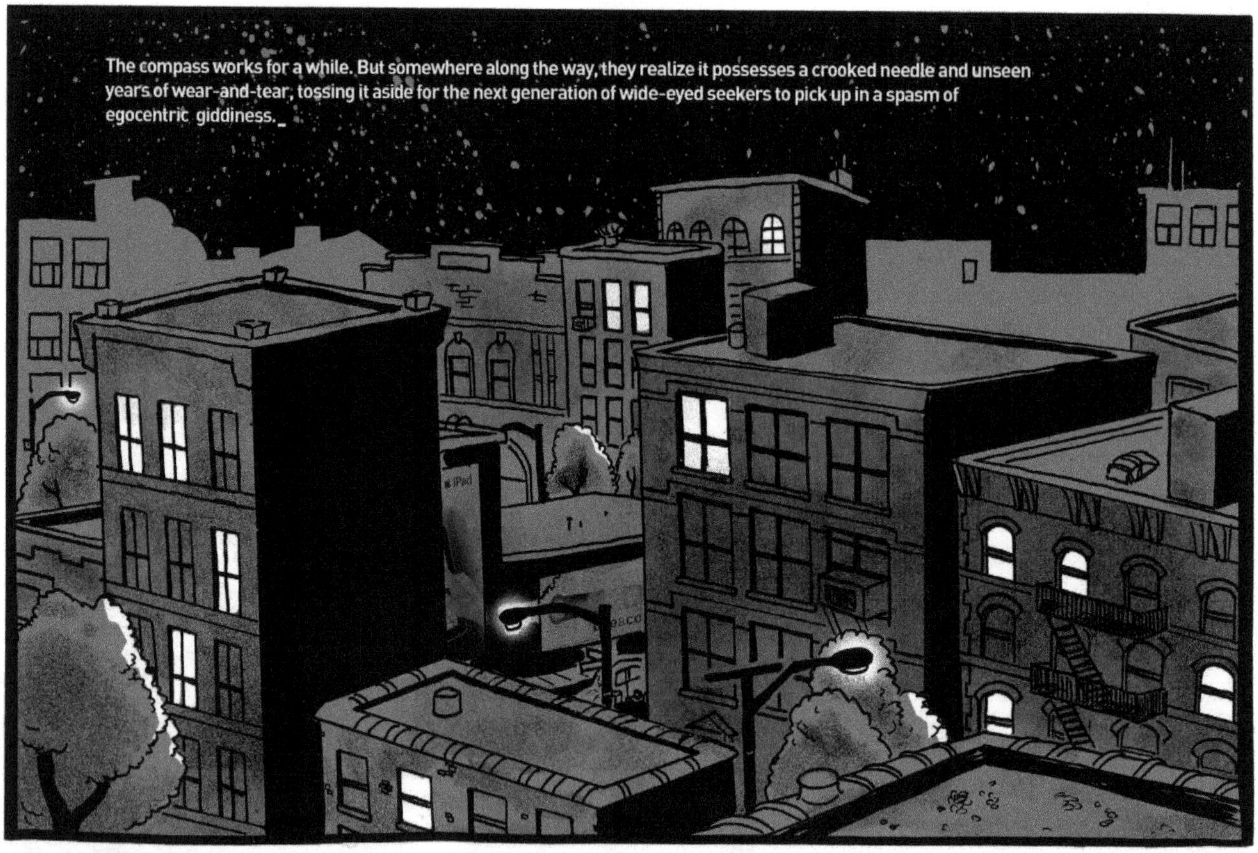

The compass works for a while. But somewhere along the way, they realize it possesses a crooked needle and unseen years of wear-and-tear, tossing it aside for the next generation of wide-eyed seekers to pick up in a spasm of egocentric giddiness._

Maybe they keep grasping because they don't know any better and are simply spent from lying to themselves.

Maybe that's how it's always been. Guess the song does remain the sameokfoerkjjkvjkjvekrkvegergklerp3e[f[3f[lblvmwlv

afsavfsrf jchwfqkjlwhlfjk3j3;flkerfl;er';''er;flqerflrfeqrkfewlqfl;qcqcllllllq34kjrcoqejfioqehfuoh c   wdhhcjq
hjcdqwfjrhejferjerjhcjwhfckjerhfkvjwerhgjkerhgkwreghreghjgthjrhiuhfirjgfigjejrgijergjke;wjerg;relg'rq;glfrlrglrlgp
ler'wgl;re';qll lgkelrwkghl;w erhkglwetkl 'wethk'ltkrylwt'tg;rleh;rlghrlllrlglqkrejrqhrrrrqrjfgw;kfjrg orkgo rekqgoorlr
oregjjgwrejgkqljrlkg ewrlkgjhekr;hgj;klejrgk;ljwklt;hjwtlhjlwrthjl;rteyhkml;rtkwjhkl;jwtkr;jherkldkfsdkfafsavfsrf
jchwfqkjlwhlfjk3j3;flkerfl;er';''er;flqerflrfeqrkfewlqfl;qcqcllllllq34kjrcoqejfioqehfuoh c   kfsdsdkfnsdkdsnksdsd dvdsfsvdfd
dsdckdokdsofksdfoskkfoswdhhcncwjdnddjfncjknfjkwfnwjfnqweowd;qwdksodkcjwinqwjxnqjsnxbnj qbsjqnsuzq eiouz
jqosijq oiej21ijdwqoujdouiawehfiuohfiusdcapSKaisjdaodajsxasnxoanxcakcasodfjasidaosfjaosvjapsvajspcsajpasjap
jfpijpfjfpifjpafpaifjaspifjapsifjipjfgipejgfipwefjgpifjdsfnsdkfnsdknvkdsvksdmfksdnlkfnajfnanjldfnakwesifkj349if-23i230if-0efj
vdsdijcadsicjdsiofjdfviodjvipodvjdfivjcivjcp jdpsicvjadopcjkvposdkjvpoadkjvpoawekfowkq-oxdkdowjcvfnvjrnfjwe ijfweifj
isfiwfjviwjvijweovciqe0fi-qeiofv0ivw 9wfgwv0wrv09wri09wri 00iwefjiwejf0iwjbieji0erfw0e
ifiwejijw0fdq-we020r3904009jvkdjsvns jvnsdk ks s vasca FSDSewrfgegfergrbggbgbgbhrbDKVSDSKgrtgkjrgijtgirtjgip SSV
dsfvejgviofjveorijerofierjf9erfierofejrfoogoejrgvorefoejwopjjxjdiqwpdko-qwkf0-wreg-egrt0okvefb-kbb k-0gtr9g
jgierjgerjgirjeijijiojdfobjswefr0er0oiqw0r2403ti934rijgerjbejgrg kgerijgeriojgierjbpjgprjfgir jgijogjeopjgpwgo jgepjkgpierjg
jpjgkeprjpgjwrpjgpwrjgkhpwrjgpjrpjgperjgperjgpejrp iokoqwqpwpppppppeoeooweiowdjiwejfqnngjnernewergok344gjgiir_

YOU SURE YOU HAVEN'T SEEN MY TEST THINGY ANYWHERE IN HERE?!
FOR THE 50TH TIME, **NO!** AND PLEASE DON'T WRECK THE BACKROOM! I JUST FINISHED CLEANING IT UP!
employees only
CAN

I LEVELED MY PLACE LAST NIGHT LOOKIN' FOR IT. NO DICE. IT HAD TO FALL IN ONE OF THESE BOXES.

THOSE TEENAGERS MUST'VE BEEN F$@&IN' AROUND WITH THE VINYL. APHEX TWIN'S IN THE CLASSICAL SECTION. MONK IN ELECTRONICA. ***IT'S A MESS!*** Y'KNOW, IT WOULDN'T HURT TO GET A CEILING CAMERA.

HA! THAT'S WHAT MARSALIS IS FOR. WHERE THE HELL IS HE?! BEEN AN HOUR SINCE WE OPENED. HE'S 'SPOSED TO ORGANIZE S#!T.

YEAH, HE'S USUALLY HERE BEFORE US. I'LL GIVE HIM A RING. HE'S BEEN ACTING WEIRD LATELY.

HEY, YOU'RE TALKIN' ABOUT MARS HERE. ***WHEN IS HE NOT?!***
pop/rock

I GOT BLISTERS ON MY FINGERS! I GOT BLISTERS ON MY FINGERS!
I GOT BLISTERS ON MY FINGERS! I GOT BLISTERS ON MY FINGERS!
BURIAL
MILES
RED HEADED STRANGER

I GOT BLISTERS ON MY FINGERS!
I GOT BLISTERS ON MY FINGERS!
ZZZ
BEASTIE BOYS

I GOT BLISTERS ON MY FINGERS!
J DILLA JAY DEE

Andy
10:11
Veronika
work
slide to answer

Andy
10:11
Veronika
work
slide to answer
I GOT BLISTERS ON MY FINGERS!

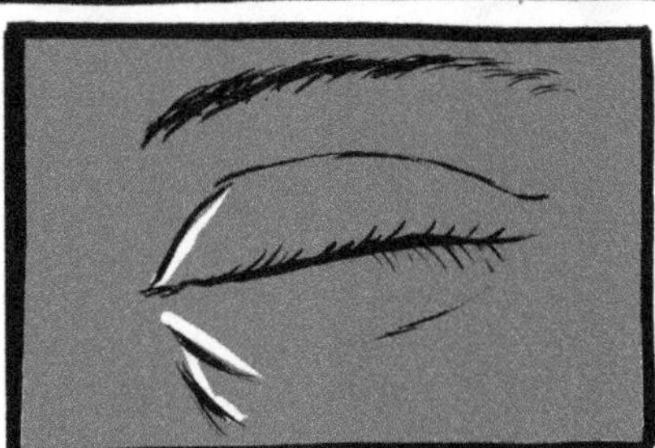

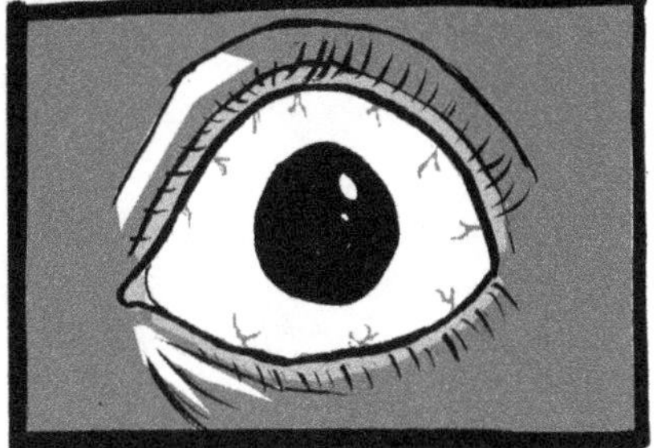

I GOT BLISTERS ON MY FINGERS! I GOT BLISTERS ON MY FINGERS!
I KNOW, R-R-RINGO!

I GOT BLISTERS ON MY FINGERS! I GOT BLISTER ON--BEEP

I'M S-SO SORRY, VERONIKA! I WAS UP L-LATE WRITING. T-T-TELL HARDY NOT TO KILL ME. THIS WILL N-N-NEVER, EVER HAPPEN AGAIN.

HAKUNA MATATA, DUDE. HE'S BUSY SPAZZING OUT OVER HIS GLUCOSE METER. YOUR TARTINESS IS LAST ON HIS MIND RIGHT NOW.

HE'S STILL HASN'T F-F-FOUND IT? A DAY IS TOO LONG TO GO W-WITHOUT ONE. C-C-CAN'T HE JUST BUY ANOTHER AT THE DRUG STORE?
HE WOULD, IF ONLY HIGHER PRICES DIDN'T "KILL HIS BUZZ." BUT IT'S BETTER TO LOSE A BUZZ THAN ANOTHER DAMN LEG!
RIGHT. I'M ON M-M-MY WAY.

BUT I JUST READ ON PITCHFORK THAT ***THE WEEKND*** IS COMING TO PLAY THE BARD NEXT THURSDAY.

NOT ACCORDING TO STEREOGUM. THEY SAY THE THURSDAY AFTER.

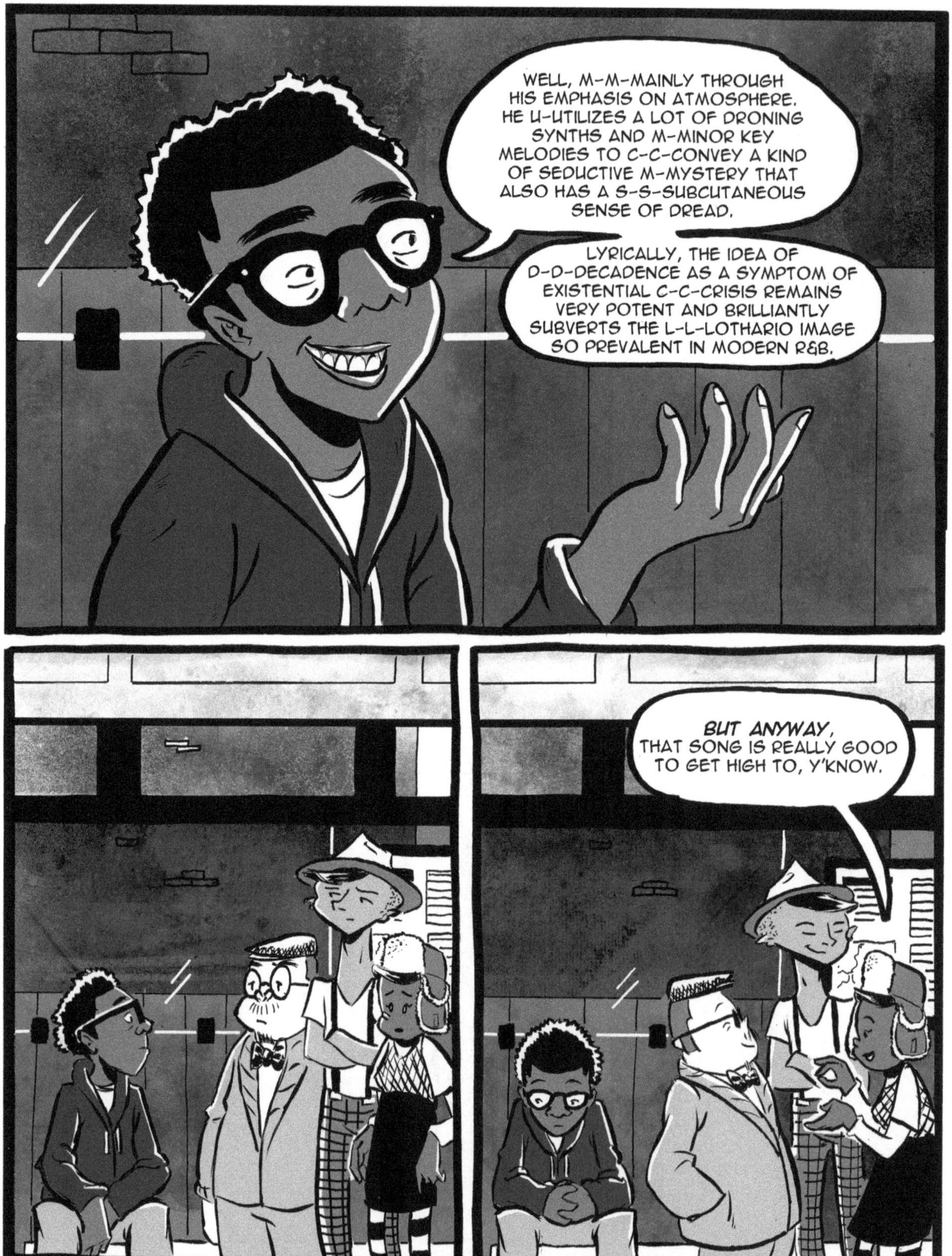

WELL, M-M-MAINLY THROUGH HIS EMPHASIS ON ATMOSPHERE. HE U-UTILIZES A LOT OF DRONING SYNTHS AND M-MINOR KEY MELODIES TO C-C-CONVEY A KIND OF SEDUCTIVE M-MYSTERY THAT ALSO HAS A S-S-SUBCUTANEOUS SENSE OF DREAD.

LYRICALLY, THE IDEA OF D-D-DECADENCE AS A SYMPTOM OF EXISTENTIAL C-C-CRISIS REMAINS VERY POTENT AND BRILLIANTLY SUBVERTS THE L-L-LOTHARIO IMAGE SO PREVALENT IN MODERN R&B.

AND NOTICE THAT LIGHTNING BOLT! WHY IS IT COVERING JUST ONE EYE? ONE EYE?! 'CUZ IT'S TIPPING US OFF TO WHO'S REALLY **MANEUVERATING** THIS SONIC NARCOTIC MACHINE.
UGH, DON'T TELL ME YOU'RE ONE OF **THEM!**

AND DIG THE TITLE. ALADDIN SANE. **A. LAD. INSANE!** PSYCHOLOGICAL ATROPHY PRECIPITATED BY FRAGMENTATION OF IDENTITY, MANIFESTED BY THE **INAUGURATION OF AN ALTER EGO.** THE WEAKER THE MIND, THE BETTER THE MIND CONTROL. ANOTHER SCHEME FROM THE SHADOWY UPPER ECHELONS.

YOU CAN'T POSSIBLY THINK BOWIE'S A TOOL FOR A NEW WORLD ORDER! **IT'S ALL JUST MUSIC, DUDE.** MAYBE SOME ANDROGYNY AND A LITTLE COKE THROWN IN, BUT IT'S MAINLY JUST HARMLESS MUSIC.

DAVID BOWIE
ALADDIN SANE

WELL, CHILD. IT PAINS ME TO PERCEIVE THE MACHINE HAS ALREADY GOTTEN TO YOU AS THEY HAVE **CONSTIPATED THE INNER REALMS OF YOUR MENTAL MIND.** OR ELSE, YOU'D SEE THE LIGHT.

WELL, BUDDY, TELL ME WHAT'S WORSE: A CONSTIPATED MIND OR **DIARRHETIC LOGIC?**

ALLOW ME TO PRESCRIBE YOU SOME *INTELLECTUAL FIBER*, THEN. THE SAME ELITES PLOTTING SCHEMES THROUGH *THIS*...

...ARE PLOTTING AGAINST OUR CHILDREN'S RIGHTS TO EDUCATION, KEEPING THEM *DEAF, DUMB AND BLIND!* WE GET ENOUGH PEOPLE TO *CONGREGATE AND COAGULATE*...

...WE CAN *DEVIATE AND DECIMATE* ANY FUTURE ATTEMPTS TO CLOSE MORE SCHOOLS.
BROTHER RAGE

RESPECT, BROTHER. THE CITY NEEDS A WAKE UP OF SOME KIND. BUT I MIGHT BE WORKING ALL NEXT WEEK THOUGH. DUNNO IF I COULD MAKE IT.

WELL, HOPEFULLY, *ALLAH WILLING*, YOUR SCHEDULE ABIDES. AND HE BE PRAISED SHOULD IT DO SO.

OUR MARCH WILL NEED ALL THE *FRESH, ACTIVE*, AND UH, *SUPPLE* MINDS IT CAN FIND.

MM-HMM... GUESS I'D HAVE TO BRING MY *GIRLFRIEND* ALONG. SHE LOVES FIGHTING FOR RIGHTS!

S-S-SORRY I'M LATE!
THE BUS TOOK F-FOREVER.
YOU SHOULD HAVE SEEN--

A-HA!
SO THAT'S THE BRUTHA YOU WERE TALKIN' 'BOUT! YEAH, MY SYNAPSES ARE SNAPPIN' NOW! THAT'S MR. GUETTA FROM THE OTHER NIGHT.
RADIOHEAD
AMY WINEHOUSE
The Mothers of Invention
FREAK OUT

WELL, GREETINGS AGAIN, YOUNGBLOOD. THE NAME'S BROTHER RAGE. UH, MARSALIS, RIGHT? I HEAR SOME PEOPLE SAY YOU'RE QUITE THE MUSIC ENCYCLOPEDIA 'ROUND THESE PARTS.
UH, YEAH, AF-F-FIRMATIVE. BRITANNICA AIN'T G-GOT S#!T ON M-M-ME. RIMSHOT.

WHO MADE THE SOUNDTRACK FOR ***SWEET SWEETBACK'S BAADASSSSS SONG?***

EARTH, WIND AND F-F-FIRE.

WHAT DAY WERE THE LAST POETS FOUNDED?

M-M-MAY 19, 1968. M-MALCOLM X'S BIRTHDAY, BY THE WAY.

HOW MANY SONGS ARE SAMPLED ON PUBLIC ENEMY'S ***FEAR OF A BLACK PLANET***?

R-ROUGHLY 140. THOUGH S-SOME S-SAMPLES REPEAT.

OUTSTANDING, MY BRUTHA! IT ALWAYS DOES MY HEART GOOD TO DISCOVER YOUTH LIKE YOURSELF POSSESSING SUCH A SOLID MENTAL MIND! THERE IS HOPE FOR THIS CITY! ***ALLAH BE PRAISED!***

UH, IT WAS N-N-NICE TALKING TO YOU, MR. RAGE. BUT I G-GOTTA WORK NOW.

WELL, I'LL BESTOW THIS UPON YOU BEFORE I MAKE MY EXIT. IN CASE YOU WERE UNINFORMED, MY SPECIAL NETWORK IS PROTESTING THE SCHOLASTIC SCHEMES AGAINST OUR SCHOOLS NEXT WEEK.
BROTHER RAGE

OUR MAYOR BELIEVES THAT CUTTING COSTS MEANS CUTTING OUT OUR CHILDREN'S DREAMS TO BETTER EDUCATION AND ECONOMIC OPPORTUNITY.

Q-Q-QUITE A WORTHY MISSION, RAGE. BUT YOU CAN HOLD ONTO THAT F-F-FLYER. I STILL GOT THE ONE YOUR G-G-GIRLFRIEND GAVE ME YESTERDAY.
The Mothers of Invention
MILES

WAIT. WHO, NOW?

YOUR GIRLFRIEND. HER NAME IS S-S-SALIMAH? DREADLOCKS, ARMY JACKET, R-R-RIPPED SHORTS? BUYS A LOT OF D-D-DE LA SOUL?

OH, SHE'S NOT MY GIRLFRIEND, BRUTHA.

B-B-BUT SHE CALLED YOU "HER B-BOYFRIEND" WHEN SHE WAS HERE YESTERDAY. SO ONE OF YOU IS INC-C-CORRECT.

NO, NO! IT'S SIMPLE, YOUNGBLOOD. SEE, UNFORTUNATELY I DON'T HAVE NO WOMAN. SALIMAH'S JUST ONE OF THE MANY, UH, ASSISTANT ACTIVISTS IN MY SPECIAL NETWORK. BUT WE ALL FEEL CLOSE LIKE WE WERE FAMILY. DIG IT, THE LIFE OF A MILITANT DOES NOT ALLOW HIM TIME FOR A REAL WOMAN.
FOR HIM, THE CAUSE IS HIS ONE AND ONLY.

AND NOW, I MUST TEND TO HER NEEDS, BY ANY MEANS NECESSARY.

WELL, UNTIL WE MEET AGAIN, ASA LAMA LAKUM, BROTHER MARSALIS. STAY BLACK!

WELL, AS YOU'LL SEE, ALL THESE LP'S NEED TO BE PUT IN THE RIGHT SECTIONS. THOSE ***ASSWIPE KIDS*** EVEN PUT SOME RECORDS IN DIFFERENT COVERS.
OF COURSE, YOU GOT THIS. YOU'RE ALWAYS METICULOUS.
TAV FALCO'S
PRINCE

HE J-JUST SAID HE DIDN'T HAVE A G-G-GIRLFRIEND.

THEY F#@$IN' STOLE ***DAFT PUNK***! AND I THOUGHT ***I*** WAS AN ASSWIPE AS A KID!

I W-WONDER IF S-S-SHE'S AWARE OF THIS PARTICULAR D-D-DETAIL?
IS WHO AWARE OF WHAT? ***WHATTA YOU STANDING AROUND FOR?!***
RADIOHEAD

S-S-SALIMAH! YESTERDAY, SHE SAID THAT R-R-RAGE DUDE WAS HER BOYFRIEND. M-MENTIONED HOW HE LIKES PUBLIC ENEMY, LAST P-POETS, ANYTHING POLITICALLY AND M-MUSICALLY INCENDIARY. BUT AP-P-PARENTLY, HE PLACES HER NEAR THE L-LOWER RUNGS OF ASSOCIATION.

SOUNDS LIKE HE'S SURREPT-T-TITIOUSLY DEVISED AGAINST HER A STRATAGEM OF ROMANTIC S-SUBTERFUGE THAT'S RIFE WITH EMOTIONAL OBFUSCATION.

AND SHE'S M-MERELY A NAIVE COG SPINNNG AWAY INSIDE THE M-MACHINE HE'S BUILT TO FUEL HIS SEXUAL NARCISSISM.

LAYMAN'S TERMS, NERD!
HE'S P-P-PLAYING HER.

WELL, NOW THAT YOU MENTION IT, HIS AURA DID SEEM A LITTLE "DOUCHE-Y" TO ME. TYPICAL POWER-CRAZY MALE. BUT WHATEVER. THAT'S HIS BUSINESS....
HOW LONG HAS THIS B-B-BEEN GOING ON? WHO ELSE IN HER C-C-CIRCLE KNOWS THE CHARADE HE'S PLAYING?
...AND THIS NEEDS TO BE YOUR BUSINESS!
IS IT WISER TO SIMPLY TURN AWAY AND ALLOW HER TO D-DISCOVER THE AWFUL TRUTH IN HER OWN T-T-TIME, RISKING HER THE EXPONENTIAL HEARTBREAK OF REALIZING HOW LONG SHE'S PLAYED THE F-F-FOOL?
OR SHOULD SOME INNOCENT, ALTRUISTIC SOUL EXERCISE A LITTLE CH-CH-CHIVALRY BY ENGAGING IN A TAUT GAME OF RELATIONAL TH-TH-THEFT?

YO!

LESS TALKY, MORE WORK-Y! THESE RECORDS AREN'T GONNA SORT THEMSELVES! NOW PLEASE, GET GOIN'! I GOTTA STOP THE ONE-LEGGED BULL FROM WRECKIN' THIS CHINA SHOP!
RADIOHEAD
weezer

Employees only
AT LEAST MY WRECKAGE IS CONFINED TO ONE PANEL! AND IT AIN'T NO CHINA SHOP! IT'S A RECORD STORE! MESS IS PART OF THE AMBIENCE! YOU'RE WELCOME!
FREAK OUT!

YOU KNOW, THERE ARE PLENTY OF DRUG STORES AROUND THE CITY THAT SELL MONITORS JUST LIKE YOURS. THIS ISN'T WORTH THE PANIC.
pop/rock
employees only
I'M PAST PANICKING, M'LADY. IN FACT, I'M CLOSER THAN EVER TO MY TREASURE BY CONTROLLING MY MIND. NOT ANTICIPATING TROUBLE, BUT *LIVING IN THE PRESENT MOMENT* WISELY AND EARNESTLY.
WHERE THE HELL'S THE INNER SLEEVE?! DO THEY KNOW HOW RARE THIS LP IS?
YEAH, I DON'T THINK BUDDHA EVER REACHED ENLIGHTENMENT BECAUSE HE WAS *CHEAP!*
EH, I CAN SEE THAT. HOW ELSE COULD HE GET FAT IF HE DIDN'T SPEND ON EATING OUT?

pop/
THAT'S WHY YOU GOT A TRIP TO THE ER COMING! 'CUZ YOU'RE USING THE SAME DAMN MONITOR SINCE '07!
UNH! NOW GET UP! YOU STUBBORN! UNH! FOOL, YOU! ARRGHH! GO MAKE A! UNH! MESS SOMEWHERE ELSE!
MONK'S DREAM THE THELO-NIOUS MONK QUAR-TET

RELAX, MON CHERIE. YOU WORRY TOO MUCH. I KNOW I'M GETTING CLOSER. THERE AIN'T ANYMORE BOXES TO OPEN.

OH YEAH, DIDN'T I JUST HEAR SLY STONE MAKE HIS LATE ENTRANCE?

FINALLY! I HAD TO BUST HIS EARDRUM TO MAKE HIM RE-SORT THE VINYL. BUT HE SHOULD BE--

LOBO

IS THAT SO, MY BRUTHA? WELL, ACCULTURATE YOURSELF TO OUR NEXT MEETING TOMORROW NIGHT. WE'LL BE GLAD TO HAVE ANOTHER HUNGRY MIND.

TH-THANKS, RAGE. I ADMIT TO NOT B-BEING CURRENT ON THE SCHOOL SITUATION. BUT M-MAYBE THE, UH, "ASSISTANT ACTIVISTS" IN YOUR GROUP COULD ENLIGHTEN ME.

LOOK UP, YOUNGBLOOD.

JM SOUTH
CONDOMINIUMS
A NEW LANDMARK COMING SOON TO GREENVILLE.
CIGARS
THE NEW DANGER.

JM SOUTH
CONDOMINIUMS
A NEW LANDMARK COMING SOON TO GREENVILLE.
BIGGER luxurious & spacious units.
BETTER quality & finishing.
HOTTEST location in the heart of the city.
Starting at $650K.

N-N-NEW PLAYGROUNDS FOR THE RICH, EH? INDEED, AN UNFORTUNATE TR-TR-TREND THESE DAYS.
SO WHERE DOES YOUR G-GROUP USUALLY CONVENE? IS IT WITHIN WALKING D-D-DISTANCE ?

THAT'S THE REASON - OR MORE PRECISELY, TREASON - OUR MAYOR'S TRYING TO SHUT DOWN OUR SCHOOLS. TO FINANCE THIS CONSUMERIST SCHEME. SEE, ITS FACADE PROMISES AN ILLUMINACIOUS TOMORROW FOR THE CITIZENRY. " LET'S MAKE OUR CITY WHOLE AGAIN! BUILD SAFER LIVING FOR THE KIDS! REDUCE THE CRIME RATE! SPLURGE AT THE FANCY, NEW QUICHE BAR!"
BUT ITS GOAL IS TO SATIATE THE BEAST OF CAPITALISM: TAX REVENUES, EXORBITATED HOUSING PRICES, DISPLACEMENT OF OUR POOREST RESIDENTS. LOSS OF HOME...LOSS OF BELONGING....LOSS OF SELF. THIS IS OUR FIGHT.

S-S-SO, WILL ALL YOUR "ASSISTANTS" BE THERE?

WHERE IS THAT SCRAWNY SONUVABITCH?
HEY VERONIKA. IS MARSALIS AROUND?
OH HEY, SEUNG-JIN.

IS HE WORKING TODAY? I WANNA ASK HIM SOMETHING. I FOUND A MUSIC PLAYER BUT IT WON'T WORK.
C'MON, PICK UP! DAMMIT, PICK UP!
BOB MARLEY

ARGGHH, SERIOUSLY?! YOU CAN IDENTIFY EVERY INSTRUMENT PLAYED ON "PET SOUNDS," BUT YOU CAN'T EVEN HEAR YOUR DAMN PHONE RINGING?!
UH, HELLO?! I WANNA KNOW IF HE CAN FIX MY MUSIC PLAYER. IT'S SUPER IMPORTANT! IS HE HERE YET?

YEAH, YEAH, JUST WAIT INSIDE, KID. IT MIGHT TAKE AWHILE TO WRANGLE HIM BACK IN.

OKEY DOKEY. HE SHOULD KNOW HOW TO FIX SOMETHING LIKE THIS.

WHO WOULD HAVE THOUGHT A FEW NEW CONDOS IN THE SCARY PART OF TOWN COULD CAUSE ***THE DUMBING DOWN OF OUR GENERATION?*** I GUESS ***L.O.L. CATS*** WAS TOO POWERFUL AND POPULAR TO DEFEAT. ***DISPLACEMENT*** IS A RATHER HARROWING END POINT, THOUGH. FAR WORSE THAN WITNESSING ***I CAN HAS CHEEZBURGER.***
ONE WAY
DELI
24 HR ATM

JUST A PERFECT DAY PROBLEMS ALL LEFT ALONE WEEKENDERS ON OUR OWN IT'S SUCH FUN ♫ ♫

BUT WHAT AND WHOM EXACTLY IS THE MAYOR DISPLACING? WHO FITS THE PROFILE OF "POOREST RESIDENT?"

MAYBE THE DOPE FIENDS THAT PLAGUE THE CITY. ***WHY NOT?*** THE LESS OF THEM, THE BETTER. GREENVILLE COULD USE A SPITSHINE.

BUT THEN AGAIN, THE CITY'S WELL-ROUNDEDNESS WOULD IMMEDIATELY VANISH WITH THE FIENDS. NOT ONLY WOULD WE LOSE OUR BALANCE ON PURELY SOCIOECONOMIC TERMS, BUT ALSO ON HETEROCULTURAL ONES TOO.
AND THE MUSIC GODS HAVE LONG KNOWN THAT ROUGHLY 95% OF THE BEST MUSIC THE WORLD HAS EVER HEARD SPRUNG FROM THE FERAL IMAGINATION OF DOPE FIENDS.

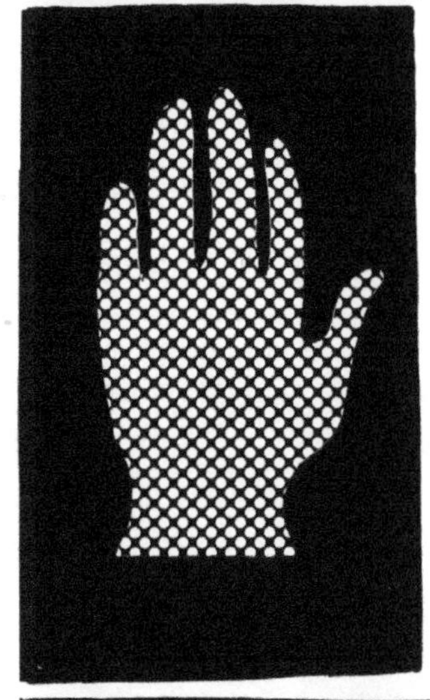

CHARLIE PARKER, MILES DAVIS, JANIS JOPLIN, JIMI HENDRIX, AMY WINEHOUSE, RAY CHARLES, KURT COBAIN, LOU REED, JIM MORRISON.

AND CRAPPY CITIES HAVE ALWAYS FACILITATED GENIUS. LIKE KURT IN ABERDEEN, OR LOU IN '70S NYC. THE LIST IS INFINITE.

AND DO WE CARE HOW THE MUSIC'S MADE? DO WE MIND THAT OUR INNUMERABLE CUES IN FASHION, LIFESTYLE AND VERNACULAR HAVE DEVELOPED FROM DECADES OF COUNTLESS, LOST SOULS SEEKING NARCOTIC OBLIVION? TO THE VERGE OF DEATH, EVEN?
NOT REALLY. AS LONG AS THE MUSIC'S GOOD. AS LONG AS WE HAVE A CATCHY DISTRACTION TO WORKOUT TO AT THE GYM.

YET, ***STEVIE WONDER*** MANAGED TO CREATE SOME OF THE MOST INFLUENTIAL POP MUSIC THE WORLD OVER AND ***NEVER*** TOUCHED ONE WHITE LINE OR NEEDLE IN HIS LIFE.... AT LEAST NOT THAT I KNOW OF. MARIJUANA, BUT THAT WAS IT. ***AND WHO DOESN'T HIT THE BUD EVERY NOW AND THEN THESE DAYS?***

SOMETHING'S STILL OFF ABOUT BROTHER RAGE'S MISSION. FIGHTING CITY GENTRIFICATION? MEH. NO GENUINE SENSE OF FEAR AMONG THE POPULACE. AND SOME MIGHT EVEN LIKE A QUICHE BAR. BUT FIGHTING ***MUSIC GENTRIFICATION?*** THAT BATTLE IS REAL! RELEVANT! NOTHING'S SCARIER THAN THAT.

YOU!

I STAND CORRECTED.

GREETINGS, M-MY EXQUISITELY TATTOOED M-MADAM!
AND IT'S IMPERATIVE THAT I SAY, C-C-CONGRATULATIONS ON REACHING YOUR 10TH STRAIGHT MONTH OF S-S-SOBRIETY!
I'M CONFIDENT YOU'RE CONQUERING ALL THOSE W-WITHDRAWAL SYMPTOMS. M-M-MOST SPECIFICALLY, EMOTIONAL OUTB-B-BURSTS.
ZIP IT, PORKY!
YOU KNOW, I AM SO F#$%ING GLAD I DON'T HAVE KIDS!
YOU AND HARDY ARE A HANDFUL ENOUGH!
NOW GET YOUR ASS IN HERE!

AND ALSO AN EXTENDED TH-THANKS FOR BEING THE IMPETUS FOR MY SHORT ABSENCE.

YOU SAID I SH-SH-SHOULD GO AND GET UN-SQUASHED, RIGHT?

VOILA AND BEHOLD!
FIRST CLASS T-T-TICKET TO UN-SQUASHED CITY!

68 w. 5th ave.
BROTHER RAGE
ACTIVIST • POET • S#!T-STARTER
YOU SAY YOU WANT A REVOLUTION?
CALL AT 1 - 800 - F. WHITEY

TH-THAT ADDRESS IS F-FOR THE ISLAMIC CENTER OF GREENVILLE. TH-THAT'S WHERE HE HAS THE WEEKLY M-MEETINGS.
68 WEST FIFTH? I THOUGHT THAT WAS THE 7-ELEVEN. WHAT, DO THEY PRAY FIRST THEN BUY THEIR PLAYBOY AFTER WORSHIP?

THEIR NEXT M-M-MEETING IS TOMORROW NIGHT. AND THEY'LL BE GOING OVER THE L-L-LOGISTICS OF THE PROTEST AT CITY HALL.THE IMPORTANT THING IS SHE WILL B-BE THERE. YOU KNOW, YOU OUGHT TO S-S-SMOKE MORE OFTEN. YOU HAVE THE B-BEST ADVICE WHEN YOU'RE LIGHTING UP.

YOU'RE DOING A B-B-BANG UP JOB RAISING US KIDS, MOTHER!
YUCK! DOMESTICITY, GROSS! NEXT TIME, GET UN-SQUASHED OFF THE CLOCK. AND CALL ME MOTHER AGAIN, I'LL SQUASH YOU! THOSE RECORDS ARE STILL WAITING FOR YOU. SO, LET GO!
WHATEVER YOU S-SAY, MOTHER!

NO DARLING, DON'T LEAVE ME! I NEED YOU, YOU HEAR?! *I NEED YOU!*

SORRY, BABE. BUT I'M A RESTLESS ARTIST. I MUST DEPART AND FOLLOW MY MUSE.

AND HOW LONG HAVE YOU BEEN SEEING THIS *"MOOSE?"*
LONG ENOUGH TO KNOW WE WERE MEANT FOR EACH OTHER. FAREWELL, BABY.

YOU GONNA MAKE ME LOMESOME WHEN YOU GO! WHAT WILL I EVER DO? *BOOHOOHOO!*

AWWW, NOW HOLD UP THERE, FOXY LADY. DON'T LET THOSE GYPSY EYES WASTE THEM TEARS ON NO HIGHWAY CHILE. COME ALONG WITH ME, BABY.
OH MY! AND WHO MIGHT YOU BE?
WHY, I'M YOUR VOODOO CHILD OF LOVE, MY SWEET ANGEL.
TAV FALCO'S
SELENA GOMEZ & THE SCENE

AND I HAVE ONLY ONE BURNING DESIRE...
SELENA GOMEZ & THE SCENE

...LEMME STAND NEXT TO YOUR FIRE!

MWAH MWAH MWAH
MWAH MWAH MWAH
MWAH MWAH MWAH
HA HA HA HA
HA HA HA HA HA

MAN, I WAS ABOUT 14 WHEN I FIRST HEARD THIS RECORD. AND I HAD THE BRITISH VERSION WITH THE, UH, *VERY SPECIAL COVER*. I TELL YA, EVEN NOW WHEN I HEAR IT, THE HAIRS ON MY ARM STILL STAND UP. I FEEL YOUNG, HOT-BLOODED, *INVINCIBLE*.
IF YA EVER WANNA KNOW HOW IT FEELS AND SOUNDS TO BE YOUNG AND WILD AT HEART, JUST SPIN THIS.
THAT JIMI GUY SOUNDS FAMILIAR. DIDN'T HE, LIKE, DIE IN A PLANE CRASH OR SOMETHIN'?

MMM-MMM. FROM DRUGS, MAINLY. HE TOOK TOO MANY, WHICH TOOK HIM TOO QUICKLY. THAT'S WHY YOU SHOULD STAY AWAY FROM THEM, LITTLEFOOT. THEY'RE VERY, VERY BAD FOR YOU.

BUT THEY HELP YOU MAKE COOL THINGS, RIGHT? *GREEN DAY* DID DRUGS ALL THE TIME AND THEIR MUSIC'S COOL. HOW CAN THEY BE BAD FOR YOU?

WELL, IT'S LIKE THIS. SOME PEOPLE DO THEM BECAUSE IT MAKES THEM FEEL GOOD, BUT THE FEELING DON'T LAST. THEY DON'T ALWAYS KNOW WHEN TO STOP DOING THEM. AND OVER TIME, DRUGS DESTROY PEOPLE'S BODIES AND THEY END UP LIKE JIMI.
UH, DID THE THERMOSTAT GET CHANGED OR SOMETHIN'? FEELS LIKE *300 DEGREES* IN HERE.

HMM. I GUESS *OREOS* ARE A DRUG, TOO. THEY MAKE ME FEEL GOOD. BUT MY PARENTS SAY THEY'RE BAD FOR ME. THEY ALWAYS MAKE ME EAT BROCCOLI AND OTHER WEIRD GREEN STUFF. *YECCHH!*
THEY MUST THINK SUGAR'LL DESTROY MY BODY LIKE YOURS. THEY'RE SILLY SOMETIMES.

UH, YEAH...SILLY.

SERIOUSLY, GUYS?! LOOK AT THIS MESS! DO I HAVE TO BABYSIT ALL OF YOU?!
RAMONES
FREAK OUT!

EASY, V! I G-G-GOT THIS. BEFORE THE D-DAY IS OVER, EVERY RECORD WILL BE IN ITS RIGHT P-P-PLACE. BACKROOM IS ALL Y-YOURS. ALL THOSE B-52 RECORDS ARE W-WAITING FOR YOUR ATTENTIVE CARE.

YEAH, YEAH, YEAH! I'M NOT STRESSING! JUST MAKE SURE THE BULL DOESN'T WRECK ANYMORE CHINA, ALRIGHT?

MARSALIS! I WAS LOOKIN' FOR YOU. CAN YOU DO ME A GINORMOUS FAVOR?

HMMMMM..... I S-SUPPOSE I COULD. BUT FIRST, YOU HAVE TO DO ME A FAVOR AND T-TELL ME HOW YOU'RE NOT IN SCHOOL AND IT'S NOT EVEN L-LUNCHTIME?

I AM IN SCHOOL, BUT WE'RE HAVING R--
R-R-RECESS? OF COURSE.
I KNOW. STRANGE WORLD, EH?

WHATEVER. L-L-LAY IT ON ME, KID.
AWESOME! BE RIGHT BACK.

I FOUND THIS MP3 PLAYER SITTING ON THE FLOOR YESTERDAY. BUT I CAN'T MAKE THIS PLAY ANYTHING.

AND SINCE YOU KNOW A LOT ABOUT MUSIC....

...MAYBE YOU COULD HELP FIX IT.

S-S-SEUNG-JIN, THIS ISN'T A M-M-MUSIC PLAYER! IT'S HARDY'S GLUCOSE METER! KID, YOU CAN'T J-J-JUST TAKE STUFF FROM THE S-STORE, THINKING IT'S F-F-FREE. IT'S NOT Y-YOURS!

GAHHH!! I'M SORRY! I'M SUPER-SORRY! I ONLY THOUGHT IT WAS FREE TO USE 'CUZ THOSE LISTENING BOOTHS WERE! DON'T TAKE ME TO JAIL!

I WOULDN'T HAVE TOOK IT IF IT WAS A IPOD! I THOUGHT IT WAS ONE OF THOSE OLD, UGLY WINDOWS-ONLY PLAYERS THAT NOBODY LIKES!

S-S-SIMMER DOWN! IT'S OKAY, KID. I'M NOT GONNA SEND YOU TO THE *P-P-PADDYWAGON.*

THANKS, MARS! I PROMISE I WON'T TAKE NOTHING FROM THIS STORE AGAIN. EVEN IF IT'S A PIECE OF JUNK!

HEY, D-DON'T SAY THAT. ALL OUR C-COPIES OF ***ROBIN THICKE'S NEW ALBUM*** WON'T T-TAKE THEMSELVES.

GEEZ! AND I THOUGHT GOING TO SCHOOL WAS TORTURE!

AT ANY R-RATE, ALL IS WELL WITH THE WORLD. AT L-L-LEAST HARDY CAN R-RELAX NOW.

UH, LOOKS LIKE HE ALREADY IS.

H-H-HARDY!
H-H-HARDY!
WAKE UP!
COME ON!
COME ON!
NO NO NO
NO NO!
V-V-
VERONIKA!
WHAT THE
HELL, DUDE?!
I'M RIGHT
HERE!
AH, STILL GOT
A P-PULSE!
COME ON, BIG GUY!
GET B-B-BACK TO US!
H-H-HARDY?
H-H-HARDY?
KER
PLOP

HOW LONG HAS IT BEEN SINCE HE CHECKED OUT?!
I DUNNO. BUT HE WAS UP JUST A M-M-MINUTE AGO.
I'LL CALL 9-1-1! IF HE STILL HAS A PULSE, THAT MEANS HE SHOULDN'T BE TOO FAR GONE!
PLEASE, COME BACK, MR ROLLINS! I SORRY I TOOK YOUR SUGAR TEST THINGY! I DIDN'T KNOW THAT'S WHAT IT WAS! PLEASE DON'T DIE ON ME LIKE THAT JIMI GUY!
YOU MEAN J-J-JIMMY LITTLE?
HENDRIX.
OH.
H-H-HARDY!!

HERE, PUT THIS WASHCLOTH ON HIS HEAD WHILE I WAIT FOR THE HOSPITAL TO PICK UP.
NO, NO, I DON'T-I DON'T NEED THAT DRIPPY THING. JUSSSSST G-GIMME SOME ASPIRIN, AND I'LL BE FINE.
GOT A H-H-HEADACHE?
JUSSSST A ITTY BITTY BIG ONE.
HMMMMM..... IT APPEARS THAT YOU JUST EXPERIENCED A HYPOGLYCEMIC SH-SHOCK. THE S-SYMPTOMS ARE USUALLY HEADACHES, SWEATING, THE SH-SHAKES AND SLURRED S-S-SPEECH. YOU NEED A S-SUGAR BOOST, QUICK!
THAT EXPLAINS WHY HE'S TALKING SO STRANGE. SOUNDS EVEN STRANGER THAN YOU.

DAMMIT. I KNEW I SHOULDA ATE SOMETHING LAST NIGHT.
BUT YOU T-TOOK YOUR INSULIN ANYWAY, D-D-DIDN'T YOU?!
LOOK, I KNOW WHAT YOU'RE GONNA SAY.
pop/rock
HARDY, YOU OF ALL PEOPLE SHOULD KNOW YOU CAN'T TAKE INSULIN WITHOUT EATING SOMETHING FIRST!
TRILL TRILL TRILL TRILL TRILL TRILL
I KNOW! I KNOW! I JUST THOUGHT I WOULD'VE F-FOUND MY THINGY BEFORE IT GOT OUT OF HAND.
TAKE SUMMA MY *JELLY BELLYS*, MR. ROLLINS! MY MOM WOULD GROUND ME IF SHE KNEW I HAD 'EM ANYWAY. YOU NEED 'EM MORE THAN ME.
THANKS, LITTLEFOOT. BUT, UH, IS THERE ENOUGH SUGAR IN *BUTTERED POPCORN* AND...*BOOGER*?

PICK UP THE LINE!
PICK THE F$#&ING LINE! ARRGGHH!
IT'S U-USELESS, V. NO AMBULANCE COMING. WE'RE IN THE WRONG P-PART OF TOWN.
TRILL TRILL
WELL, WHAT GOOD ARE THEY, THEN?! THEY CAN'T BE THAT SCARED OF THIS PART OF TOWN! THIS IS RIDIC---
911, WHAT'S THE NATURE OF YOUR EMERGENCY?
HOLY CRAP! THEY PICKED UP!
HELLO?! 911! ANYONE THERE?!
NO! NO! DON'T GO! I NEED AN AMBULANCE!
MY BOSS JUST PASSED OUT FROM A DIABETIC SOMETHING OR OTHER.
TELL ME WHAT IS YOUR LOCATION, MA'AM?
BLACKWAX BOULEVARD. 716 CYPRUS AVENUE.
OK, MA'AM. NOW, HOW OLD IS YOUR BOSS?
IN HIS MID 50'S. PLEASE HURRY!
CALM DOWN, MA'AM. NOW I'M GOING TO ASK YOU A FEW MORE QUESTIONS...

HOW LONG HAS IT BEEN SINCE YOUR BOSS PASSED OUT?
I DUNNO, LIKE, I GUESS MAYBE A COUPLE MINUTES?

HE'S CONSCIOUS NOW BUT HE'S STILL SHAKY AND HE COULD GO BACK OUT AGAIN AT ANY TI---
SLOW DOWN, MA'AM. WE'RE SENDING PARAMEDICS RIGHT NOW. JUST STAY ON THE LINE.

OK. THANK YOU! THANK YOU!

SEE? THEY'RE ON THEIR WAY. WHERE THERE'S LIFE, THERE'S HOPE.
JUST W-WAIT FOR IT. IN 3, 2...

NOW MA'AM, DID YOU SAY "716 CYPRUS AVENUE?"
YES, THAT'S RIGHT. BLACKWAX BOULEVARD. IT'S PAST HENRY'S CHICKEN SHACK BUT BEFORE YOU GET TO SOO-YI'S BEAUTY SUPPLY.

CHICKEN SHACK..... AND BEAUTY STORE? ARNIE, 10-22 THAT!
-CLICK-
....

HELLO?!
....
....
HELLO?!
T-T-TOLD YA.
BUT HONESTLY, I'M Q-QUITE SURPRISED MYSELF THAT THEY DIDN'T F-F-FALL FOR THE "W-WHITE WOMAN IN DISTRESS" VOICE.
IT'S USUALLY INF-FALLIBLE.
CALL DISCONNECTED

I COULD GO TO THE STORE AND GET SOME MORE CANDY! I'LL RUN SUPER FAST!
employees only
SEUNG-JIN, THAT'S ON THE OTHER SIDE OF TOWN. THERE'S NO TIME. HE NEEDS AN AMBULANCE! NOW!
CHOMP CHOMP NOM NOM
H-HARDY, D-D-DON'T YOU HAVE SOMETHING IN YOUR APARTMENT THAT CONTAINS A L-LOT OF SUGAR? ANYTHING SWEET OR SACCHRINE?!
I WISH. BUT I DIDN'T GET TO THE STORE YESTERDAY. BUSY TRYING TO FIND MY TEST THINGY.
AND I USED UP ALL MY STASH OF SWEETS I USUALLY KEEP IN THE BACKROOM.
FREAK OUT!
Karmin
TOM WAITS
Karmin
HELLO

BUT LIKE I S-SAID, AN ASPIRIN WILL GET ME STRAIGHT AGAIN. SO SCREW THE AMBULANCE! I FEEL F-F-FI---
I F-F-FEEL F-I-I-I-I-N-E...
BAP!
CRAP! I KNEW IT! HE'S GOING TO THE HOSPITAL NOW! WE'RE WASTING TOO MUCH TIME!
BUT THE AMBULANCE WON'T COME, WILL THEY?!
I'LL CALL A CAB, THEN! THAT'S OUR ONLY HOPE AT THIS POINT! NOW, HELP ME GET HIM UP!
Karmin
L-L-LADIES, PUT HIM BACK D-DOWN!
Karmin
I HAVE F-FOUND THE MEDICINE!

EAR PHONES ARE ON THE HEAD.
ARE YOU SUPER SURE THIS IS GONNA WORK?

P-P-POSITIVE. IT'S JUST LIKE THE P-POET NOVALIS SAID...

"EVERY DISEASE IS A MUSICAL P-P-PROBLEM; EVERY CURE IS A MUSICAL S-S-SOLUTION."

CLICK

SET THE STYLUS TO TRACK T-T-TWO.
SETTING STYLUS.

CRACKLE

OH...YEAH UH, COME ON.....YEAH
THIS IS MORE THAN
THE TYPICAL KINDA THING
FELT THE JOLTS IN MY BONES
WHEN YOU WERE TOUCHING ME
OH, OH DIDN'T WANT TO TAKE IT SLOW
IN A DAZE, GOING CRAZY,
I CAN BARELY THINK
YOU'RE REPLAYING IN MY BRAIN,
FIND IT HARD TO SLEEP

HE'S STILL NOT MOVING. DO SOMETHING, MARS!
THAT'S C-CUZ WE HAVEN'T REACHED THE C-CHORUS.
VERONIKA, B-B-BLAST IT!
OH, OH WAITING FOR MY PHONE TO BLOW.... UH, OH, YEP

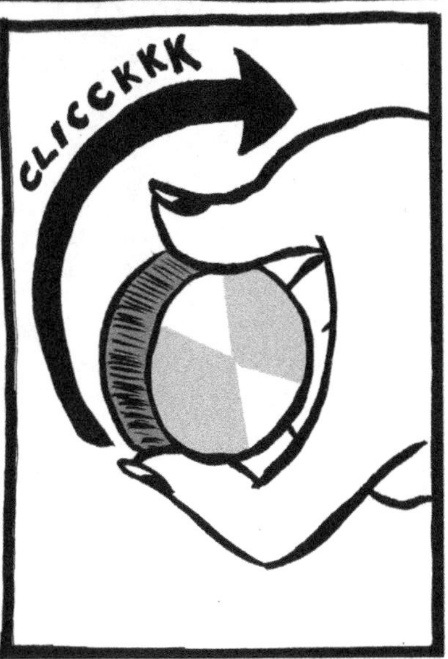
CLICCKKK

SEE I'VE BEEN WAITING
AAAAALLLLL
DAAAAAY
FOR YOU TO CALL ME
BABY
SO LET'S GET UP, LET'S GET ON IT
DON'T YOU LEAVE ME BROKENHEARTED

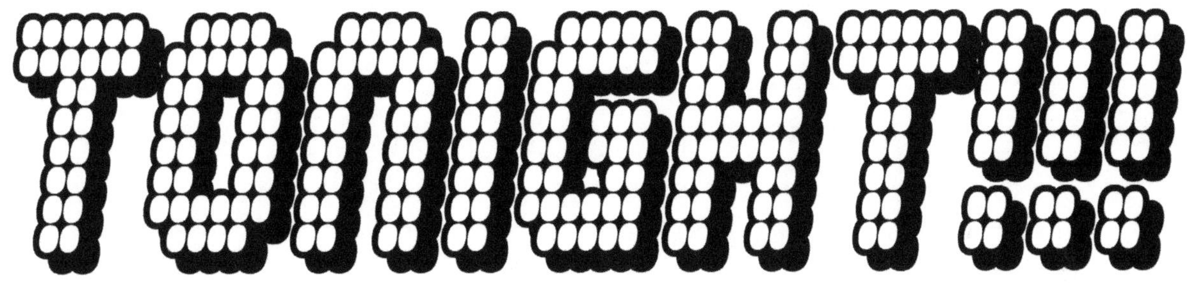
TONIGHT!!!

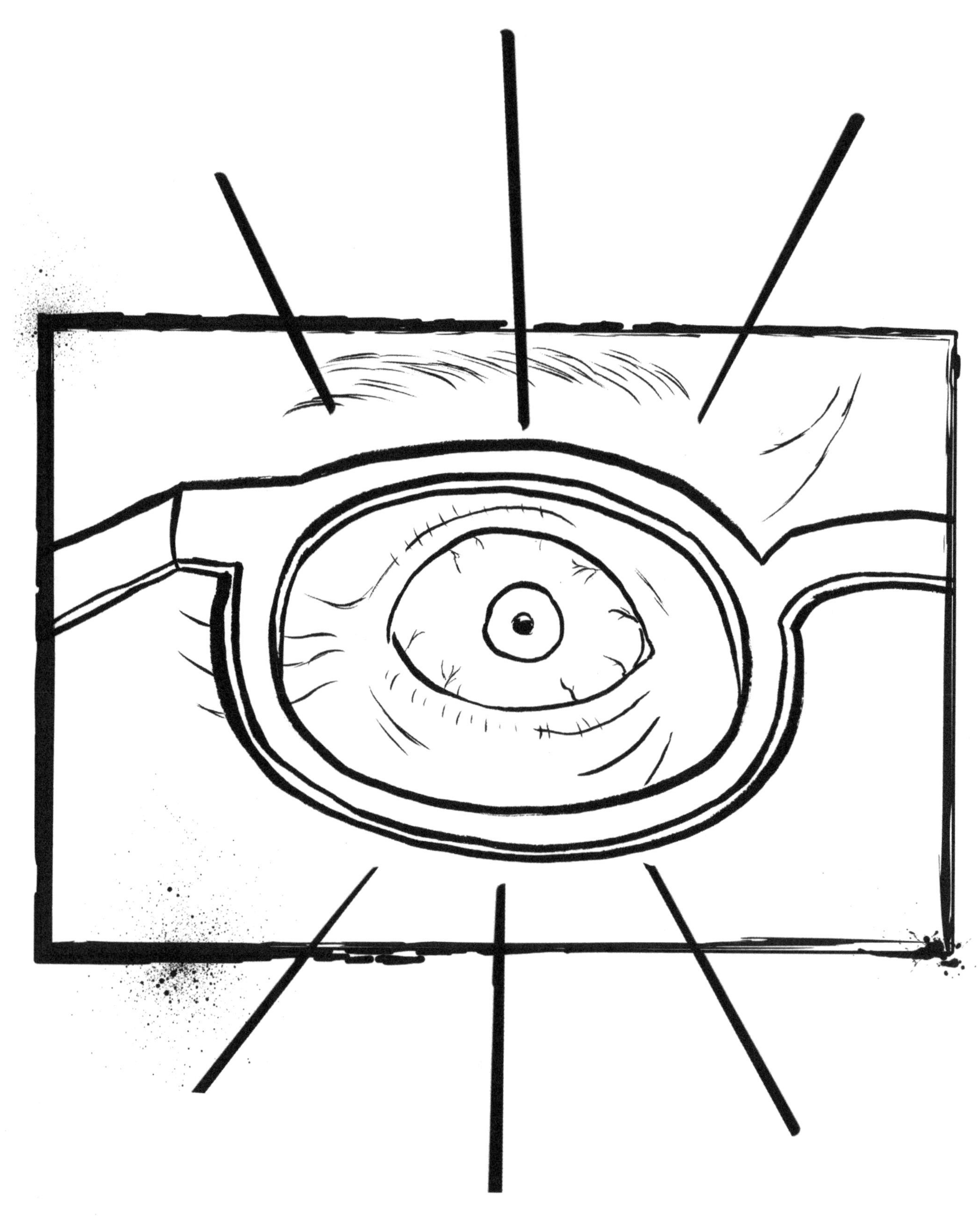

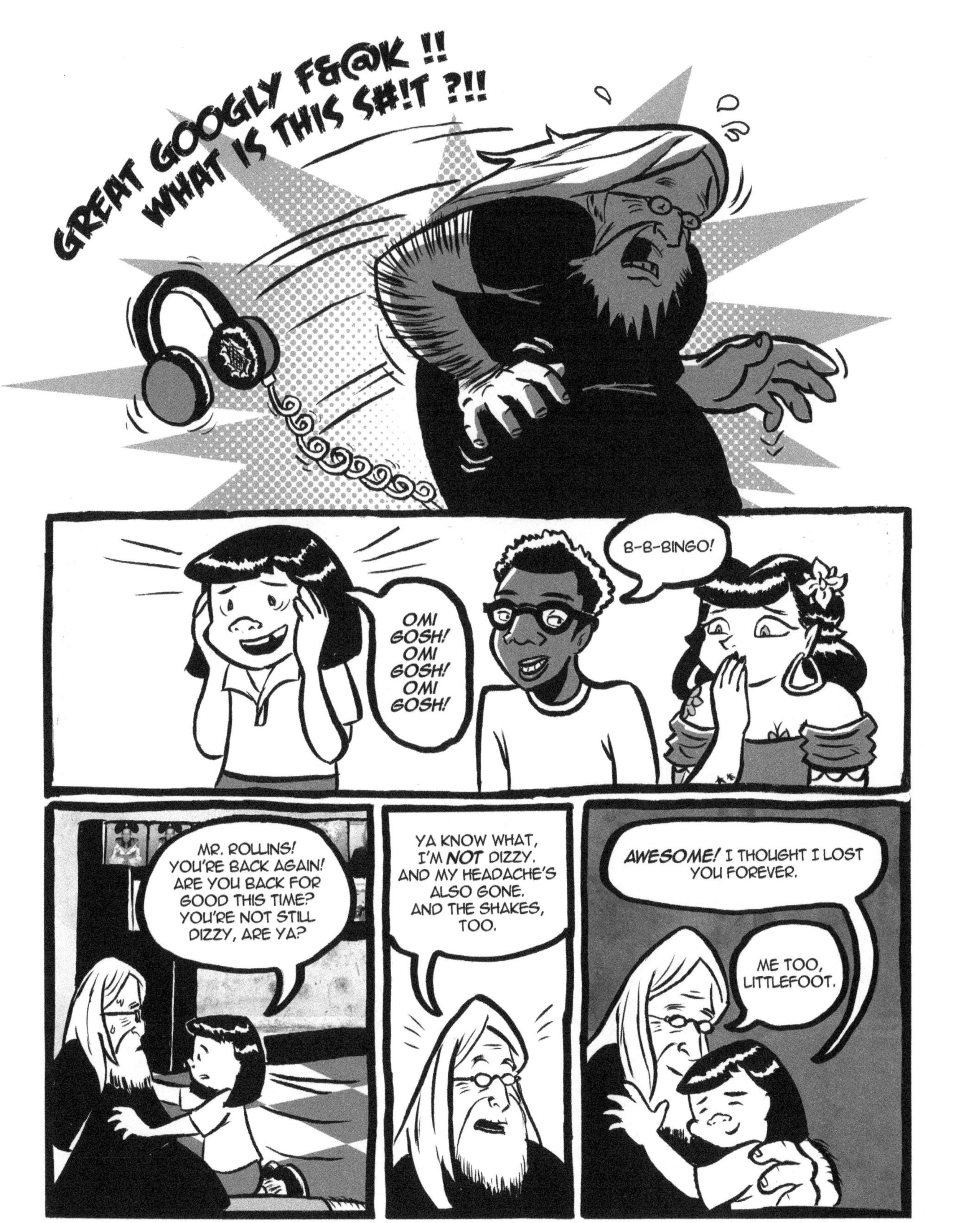

GREAT GOOGLY F&@K !!
WHAT IS THIS S#!T ?!!

OMI GOSH! OMI GOSH! OMI GOSH!

B-B-BINGO!

YA KNOW, MARS, IF YOUR WRITING CAREER DOESN'T WORK OUT, YOU'D MAKE A SUPER GREAT DOCTOR.

YEAH, DUDE. HOW THE HELL DID YOU DO IT?

WELL, IT'S Q-QUITE SELF-EXPLANATORY. THESE DAYS, THERE'S NO D-D-DIFFERENCE BETWEEN DR. PEPPER, JELLY BELLYS, AND THE T-T-TOP 40.
ALSO, TO A M-M-METAL DISCIPLE SUCH AS YOURSELF, NOTHING'S MORE J-J-JARRING TO THE SENSES THAN HEARING W-WHITE GIRLS TRYING TO RAP.

HAR HAR. THE SCOURGE OF WHITE FEMALE RAPPERS. WOE TO THE WORLD! NOW CAN WE SEE WHAT A REAL DOCTOR SAYS? PLEASE?!

#4

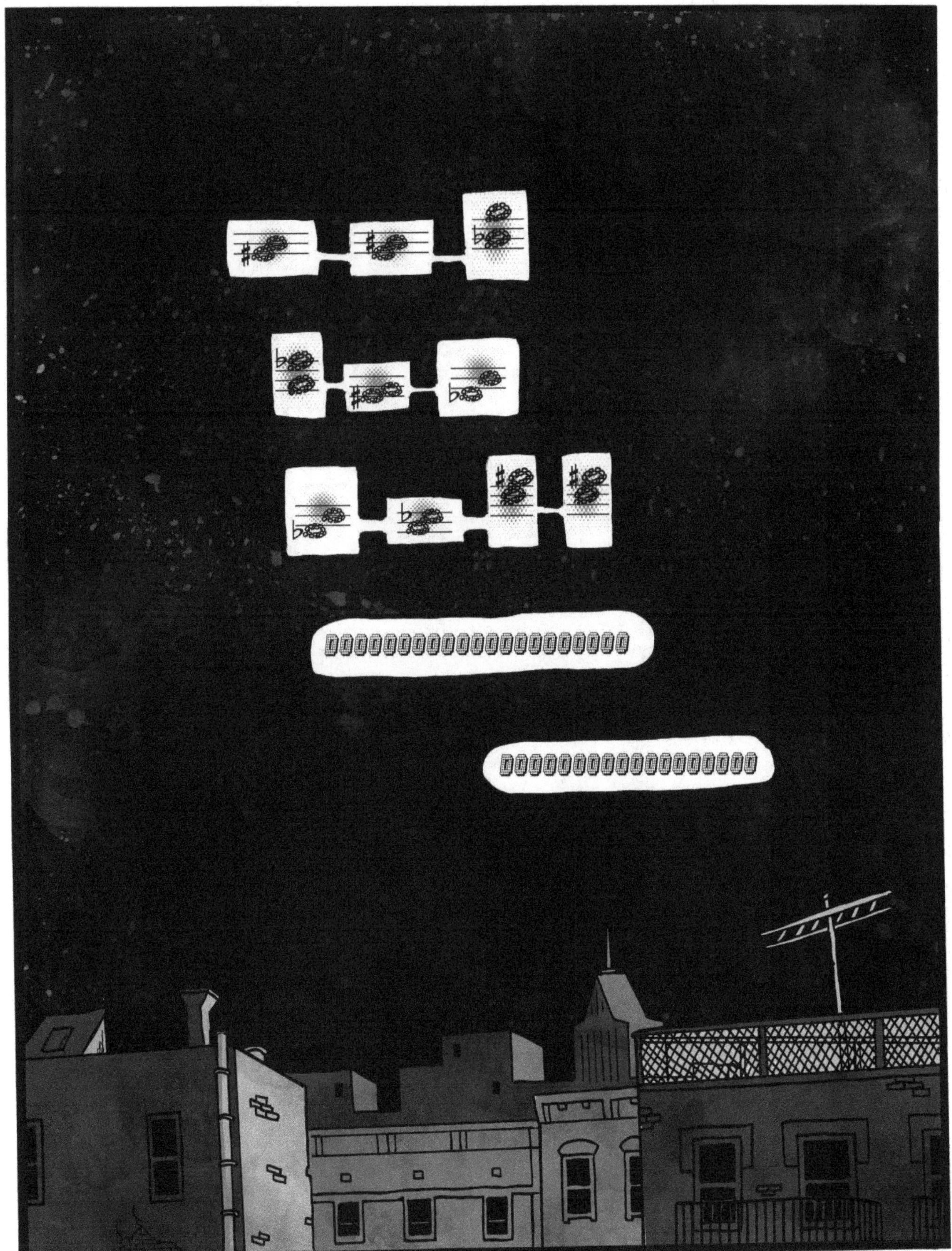

OOOOOOOOOOOOOO--
HELLO... AND THANK YOU FOR CALLING THE GREENVILLE GRAPEVINE...

...WINNER OF THE 2007 AMERICAN NEWSWEEKLY AWARD FOR BEST PUBLICATION. FOR ENGLISH, PRESS ONE. PARA ESPANOL, OPRIMA DOS.
PACE
PACE

IF YOU KNOW YOUR PARTY'S EXTENSION, PLEASE DI--

WE ARE TRANSFERRING YOUR CALL. PLEASE WAIT ON THE LINE.
PACE
PACE

...As he rises to her apology...

...Anybody else would surely know...

...He's watching her gooooo...

...But what a fool BELIEEEEEEEEEEEEEEEEEEEVES HE SEEEEEEEEEEEEEEEEEES...

...NO WISE MAN HAS THE POWER!

...to reason awaaaaaay...
R-REALLY? THAT S#!TTY SONG? NO W-WONDER YOUR CIRCULATION'S DWINDLING.
KER-PLUNK!

YOU HAVE REACHED THE HR DEPARTMENT OF THE GREENVILLE GRAPEVINE. SORRY, BUT WE ARE UNAVAILABLE TO TAKE YOUR CALL AT THE MOMENT.

AFTER THE TONE, PLEASE LEAVE A DETAILED MESSAGE WITH YOUR NAME AND PHONE NUMBER...

...AND WE WILL GET BACK TO YOU SHORTLY. THANK YOU.

GREENVILLEGRAPEVINE.COM | FREE
JUNE 4-10 2015 | VOLUME 39 | ISSUE 7
THE GREENVILLE GRAPEVINE
M.I.'ye.
How 808s Ruined Mr. West's Music Mojo
by Chester Vick

BEEP
HELLO, THIS IS M-M-MARSALIS J. PARKER. I'M PERFORMING A W-WEEKLY FOLLOW-UP CALL REGARDING YOUR PAPER'S RECENT AN-N-NOUNCEMENT SEEKING MUSIC WRITERS...
...I EMAILED MY R-RESUME AND WRITING SAMPLES TO ALL R-RELEVANT EMAIL ADDRESSES ABOUT FIVE W-WEEKS AGO AND WAS NEVER S-SENT CONFIRMATION THAT MY APPLICATION WAS RECEIVED.
[MUSIC]
WE'RE HIRING!
BEER BEER NEW RELEASE HAPPY HOUR
FEATURING NEW RELEASES EVERY WEEK
3:00 TO 7:00 TUES DAYS
MUSIC RECORD SHOP
IN ADDITION TO R-ROUTINE MONITORING OF MY PERSONAL INBOX, I HAVE CONSISTENTLY SCOURED ALL PAGES OF YOUR W-WEBSITE FOR POSSIBLE UPDATES, AND THE RESULTS WERE WANTING.
MUSIC EDITOR-IN-CRIME CHESTER VICK
GREENVILLE GRAPEVINE 39
I ASSUME THE HIRING P-PROCESS CAN BE QUITE RIGOROUS, SO I UNDERSTAND WHY YOUR RESPONSE HAS BEEN D-DELAYED.
AT ANY R-RATE, I BELIEVE THE LITERARY INTEGRITY OF MY APPLICATION RENDERS A PROMPT CONFIRMATION AS W-WORTHWHILE. YOU CAN CALL ME AT—
BEEP
TO GO BACK TO THE PREVIOUS MENU, PLEASE PRESS ONE. FOR ALL OTHER OPTIONS, PLEASE PRESS STAR.
$@!?

?
BE OUR FRIEND

LOVE
forever changes

FOREVER CHANGES
LOVE
STEREO
SIDE ONE

Sorry, Billy Shears, for this inconvenient truth.

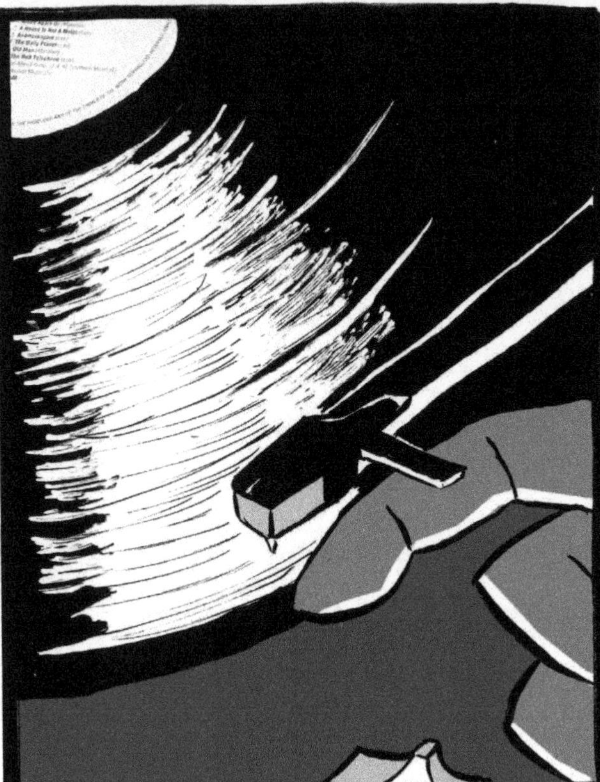

VOLUME
MIN
MAX

But the mantle for Most Important Album of the '60s belongs to Forever Changes, dreamed up by Arthur Lee and his LA-based band Love. Emerging in late fall of '67, that lysergic year where the feels were as electric as the music, Forever Changes is a nearly all-acoustic but fully prescient masterpiece that would make Janus proud. And no, dear friends, not Janis our beloved "pearl." But Janus, the Roman god of beginnings, transitions and endings. It is the sound of rats fleeing the sinking, Day-Glo-coated ship of Flower Power and Free Love.
YEAH... I SAID IT'S ALL RIGHT... I WON'T FORGET... ALL THE TIMES I WAITED PATIENTLY FOR YOU...
TAP TAP TAP

You'll hear it as the melody and harmonies of "Alone Again Or" mingle like a bull and its matador. Or when the specter of Vietnam in "The Daily Planet" mutates the black-and-white code of war into grey-and-red. Even as the blood trickles into the charred streets of Watts and the Sunset Strip on "The Red Telephone." **Turmoil lurks everywhere.**
EARLIER THAT DAY...

JOHNSON NEWITT
BUY SELL TRADE LPs CDs TAPES

CLICK

HEY, YOU'RE OPEN! WAS YESTERDAY A HOLIDAY OR SOMETHING? I CAME BY, BUT DIDN'T SEE ANYONE.

WE CLOSED EARLY, LEE JIM. TOOK HARDY TO THE URGENT CARE CENTER.
WE'RE KINDA BUSY. SO JUST LEAVE THE MAIL ON THE TABLE, ALRIGHT?

URGENT CARE? SORRY TO HEAR. IS EVERYTHING GOOD, THOUGH?

OH, OF COURSE, MAN. THEY JUST DID THE USUAL S#!T. TESTED SOME BLOOD AND PEE. TOLD ME TO WATCH IT NEXT TIME. I WAS OUT THE DOOR *EASY.*
PROMO PROMO, CREDIT CARD, PROMO...

TH-THEY SAID IF HE DOESN'T ADOPT BETTER C-C-CONSUMPTION HABITS, HIS P-PIROUETTE ON THE PRECIPICE OF DEATH W-WILL HAVE A HORRIFYING CODA. *DIET OR DIE, FOR THE P-PLEBEIAN.*

YOU KNOW, I THINK I HEARD LONG AGO THAT NICK JONAS HAS DIABETES TOO. THAT REMINDS ME, YOU GUYS HAVE ANY OF HIS OLD STUFF?

MAYBE VERONIKA CAN SHOW ME WHERE YOU MIGHT HAVE--
BYE, LEE JIM!

PROMO, PROMO, F#$@IN' PROMOS!

Y'KNOW, YA COULDA SAVED THE GAS COMING HERE YESTERDAY BRINGING THIS S#!T! WHAT WAS THE POINT?!

UH, YOU DID GET SOME NEW COUPONS FROM HENRY'S CHICKEN SHACK. FREE TUB OF DIPPING SAUCE WITH A 12-PIECE. SO, MEA CULPA?
FREE TUB OF DIPPING SAUCE
HENRY'S
CHICKEN SHACK

HEH, P-P-PERHAPS THAT DEAL WOULD ENTICE 24 HOURS AGO. BUT I SUSPECT THAT HIS NEW D-D-DIETARY REGIMEN WOULD EXCLUDE--

GREAT GOOGLY F#@K! A WHOLE TUB?

EASY, BOY! THERE'S WAAAAYY BETTER CHICKEN AND DIPPING SAUCE DOWN AT MERCHANT JACK'S.
RIIIIIGHT! THE PLACE WITH ALL THAT ORGANIC KALE S#!T.

AND ORG-G-GANIC MEATS, VEGETABLES, DAIRY. NATURALLY SWEETENED D-DESSERTS, EVEN.

YAH, STUFF YOU WON'T DIE FROM.
UGH, THEIR FOOD IS TOO WHITE, EVEN FOR ME!

JUST TO THROW IN MY TWO CENTS, I LIKE MERCHANT JACK'S MYSELF. VERY HOT LITTLE MARKET. ALL THE YOUNG, HIP TEENAGERS SHOP THERE...
...SOME OF THE RIPEST, FRESHEST STUFF YOU'LL EVER SEE.
MILES

UH YEAH, N-N-NOTHING QUITE MATCHES THEIR PRODUCE SELECTION.
OH, THAT'S ALSO TOPS. SEE YA TOMORROW!

YOU HAVEN'T EVEN TRIED MERCHANT JACK'S YET! DO YOU KNOW HOW MANY YEARS THE KALE ALONE COULD ADD TO YOUR LIFE?
?

P-PRECISELY. JUST ASK BILL WARD AND GEEZER BUTLER FROM BLACK SABBATH, LIFELONG V-V-VEGANS. I'M QUITE ASSURED THEY F-FREQUENT THERE ALL THE TIME.
weezer

I SAY A SHOPPING TRIP IS IN ORDER. WE GET YOU EATING RIGHT, STARTING TODAY! NO EXCUSES, NO ESCAPE!

H-H-HELLO?! EARTH TO HARDY?

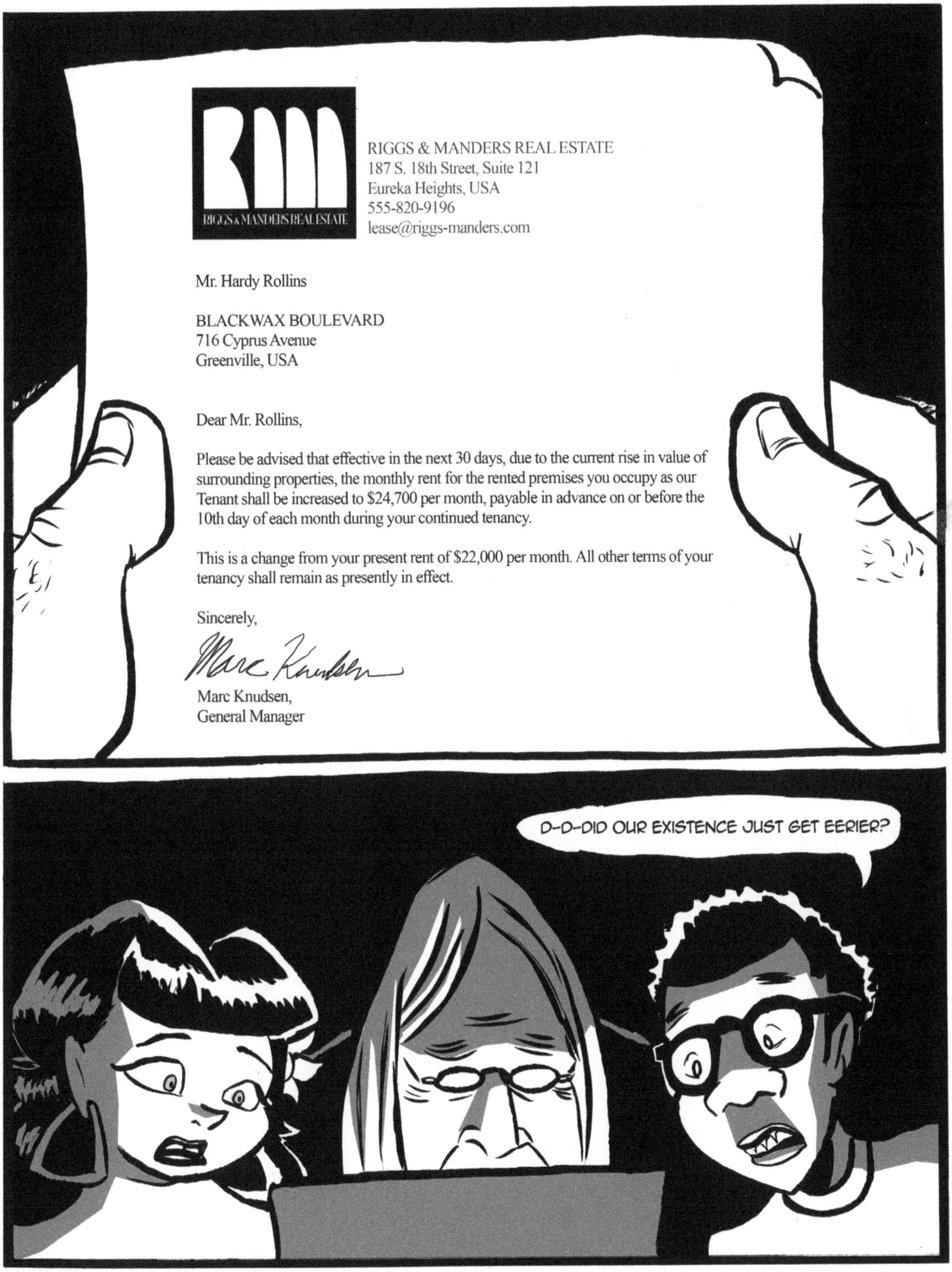

RIGGS & MANDERS REAL ESTATE

RIGGS & MANDERS REAL ESTATE
187 S. 18th Street, Suite 121
Eureka Heights, USA
555-820-9196
lease@riggs-manders.com

Mr. Hardy Rollins

BLACKWAX BOULEVARD
716 Cyprus Avenue
Greenville, USA

Dear Mr. Rollins,

Please be advised that effective in the next 30 days, due to the current rise in value of surrounding properties, the monthly rent for the rented premises you occupy as our Tenant shall be increased to $24,700 per month, payable in advance on or before the 10th day of each month during your continued tenancy.

This is a change from your present rent of $22,000 per month. All other terms of your tenancy shall remain as presently in effect.

Sincerely,

Marc Knudsen,
General Manager

"I don't know if I am living
Or if I'm supposed to be.
Sometimes my life is so eerie."

- Love, The Red Telephone|

Turmoil is that great white shark scanning the waters above for a distracted swimmer, slowly revealing its eerie form as it closes in on the mindless prey.

Arthur Lee and co. are the shoreside Cassandras screaming "SHARK, SHARK! GET OUT OF THE WATER!" And ignorance would be forgiven as the lush tapestry of guitars, strings and horns osmose into the marrow. The hypnotic acoustics ebb and flow like the textures – musical, emotional, take your pick! – of a steady world right before reaching a bloody turning point.

Warnings and harbingers aren't exactly the types of medicine ingested by daydream believers. First, all promises of getting laid in the name of "love and freedom, man!" go straight out the window. And second, after turning on and dropping out for the better part of a decade, too much responsibility and sobriety must be re-learned. Which is why Forever Changes was a commercial disaster, peaking only at #154 on the Billboard 200 in 1968. The breaking news of Cronkite was no match for the gospel of a lava lamp.

NO, NO! NOT ANOTHER LOAN!

LISTEN, THE BANK GIVES WAY MORE BREAD TO BUSINESSES SMALLER THAN US. AND ASSLOADS MORE TO THOSE "SURROUNDING PROPERTIES." 2700 BUCKS ARE JUST A PINCH TO 'EM.
pop/rock

BUT THREE LOANS OVER F-F-FOUR YEARS?! THEY'RE STILL H-HOUNDING US FOR WHAT WE OWE NOW! AND D-D-DON'T FORGET THE INTEREST AND LATE FEES.

WE STILL GOT 30 DAYS. I'LL GO TO THE BANK TODAY AND WORK MY MAGIC. THEY KNOW WE'RE STILL GOOD FOR ANOTHER ONE.

NOT SO FAST, MR. COMA! DOCTOR TOLD YOU TO REST EASY, WHICH YOU SHOULD BE DOING RIGHT NOW. YOU'RE LUCKY YOU DIDN'T GET ANY BRAIN DAMAGE FROM THAT LAST EPISODE.

EX-X-XACTLY. ONLY POSSIBLE DAMAGE IS TO THE S-SOUL WHEN YOU CAME TO. TH-THAT'S HOW SYNTH-POP KILLS. ON THE INSIDE.

WHO'S BUYING ALL THE RECORDS THESE DAYS?! DIDN'T VINYL JUST HAVE A MONSTER YEAR LAST YEAR?! WHERE ARE *THOSE* CUSTOMERS? WHAT ARE THEY BUYING? AND WHY IS *MY* STORE MISSING THE F#&$IN' PARTY?!

AND GET YER DAMN HANDS OFF ME! AND DON'T LOOK AT ME WITH THAT FACE LIKE I'M SOME OLD, F#&$IN' CRIPPLE!
employees only

OKAY.... WELL... I'M **NOT** OLD!

I'M NOT...

GO HOME, ALRIGHT? TAKE A DAY OFF.
...OLD.
EX-X-XACTLY. THE LAST THINGS YOUR B-BLOOD SUGAR NEEDS ARE MORE STRESS HORMONES.

The jet-black prospect of Death didn't move album units as easily as peaceful protest or drug-fueled hedonism. Yet, I dare you to present a list of the greatest agents of change where death doesn't beat everything–peace, poon and pot–by a wide margin. Eventually, epiphany arrived to the Aquarius age like a hot, Memphis shell from a thirty-aught-six. "Forever" proved mercurial.|

BUT THE CLEARANCE STUFF STILL NEEDS ROTATING, AND THE COMEDY SECTION NEEDS RESTOCKING, AND--
AND MAMA'S IN THE FACTORY AND SHE AIN'T GOT NO SHOES!
OPEN
P-PRECISELY. YOU'RE ROCKIN' WITH THE B-BEST, HARDY. RELAX!

AND SOMEBODY'S GOTTA STAY AND CLOSE TONIGHT.

YOU GOT IT. DONE AND DONE.
RIGHT. WE'LL STAY AND--

C-CLOSE?!

HERE'S THE KEYS. THE MIDDLE ONE'S FOR THE STORE. JUST DON'T LET IT BURN DOWN.

HEY, I SMOKED 'EM ALL WAITING OUTSIDE URGENT CARE. NOW WOULD YOU JUST RELAX?

HEH, Y'KNOW, THIS IS KINDA LIKE WHEN **OZZY LEFT SABBATH** FOR A WHILE. THEY CARRIED ON 'TIL HE CAME BACK.
BOOP BOOP BEEP
CLICK
BUZZ

K-K-KINDA. I MEAN, IF YOU T-TAKE OUT OZZY'S HABIT FOR **BOOZE AND BLOW** AND G-GETTING REPLACED BY **DIO** AND AN **18-YEAR ABSENCE** FROM THE BAND. THEN, YEAH, K-K-KINDA.

THANKS, GUYS. AND I **WILL** HAVE A PLAN.

AND A LEMON CHICKEN SALAD, SPECIALLY DELIVERED BY **MERCHANT JACK!**
$@#!?$!

TH-TH-THIS WHOLE THING DOESN'T JIBE WITH ME. HARDY'S G-GOTTA BE MORE ***THOUGHTFUL*** WITH THINGS OF THIS N-N-NATURE.

RIGHT? THAT'S WHY I'M HEADED TO MERCHANT JACKS'S TO GET HIM EATING RIGHT ***PRONTO.*** A GUY AT HIS AGE CAN'T AFFORD TO PISS AWAY TIME OR HIS HEALTH.

N-NO, I MEAN HIS ***MUSICAL ANALOGY.*** HOW S-SAD AND INACCURATE TO BE COMPARED TO POST-OZZY SABBATH. THEY S-SUCKED WHEN HE LEFT ***AND*** WHEN HE CAME BACK. WE'RE HOPEFULLY MORE LIKE MID-NINETIES ***RED HOT CHILI P-PEPPERS***, WHEN FRUSCIANTE LEFT. THEY WERE MORE P-POPULAR THAN EVER WHEN HE RETURNED.

YEAH. THEN HE LEFT AGAIN AND THEY WENT BACK TO SUCKING.
W-W-WELL, NOW YOU'RE OVERTHINKING IT.

W-W-WELL,
THINK ABOUT HOLDING ONTO THESE KEYS AND MANNING THE STORE WHILE I GET HARDY SOME GROCERIES. I'LL BE BACK IN 15.

W-W-WAIT UP!
VERONIKA, I C-C-CAN'T CLOSE TONIGHT. YOU'LL HAVE TO D-DO IT.

I HAVE A P-PRIOR ENGAGEMENT TONIGHT, REMEMBER? AND IT'S OF THE MOST V-VITAL POLITICAL IMPORTANCE THAT I KEEP MY COMMITMENT.

ARE YOU F$#@IN' KIDDING ME?! AFTER WHAT HAPPENED YESTERDAY?!

IT'S V-V-VERY IMPORTANT! THE FUTURE GENERATION'S EDUCATION C-C-COULD BE AT STAKE HERE! YOU KNOW THE MUNICIPAL REVENUE THAT COULD G-GO TO THE SCHOOL DISTRICT?

IT'S REALLY FOR THOSE "S-SURROUNDING PROPERTIES." CONDOS, BICYCLE SHOPS, ANOTHER F-F-FROYO. IT'S BEEN GETTING WORSE FOR THE PAST FOUR YEARS.

AND I FIRMLY BELIEVE IT'S MY D-DUTY TO PARTICIPATE IN PRESERVING THE SCHOLASTIC WELFARE OF OUR N-NEIGHBORHOOD. THIS IS B-BIGGER THAN ME.

HOW MUCH FROYO HAVE *YOU* HAD OVER THE PAST FOUR YEARS?

HEY, M-M-MY DIETARY HABITS ARE IRRELEVANT IN THIS MATTER! *THIS IS ABOUT THE K-K-KIDS!*

OPEN
FREE
OOOPH! L-LET GO! LOOK, EVEN IF HE GOES C-C-COMATOSE AGAIN, IT'S NOTHING C-CALVIN HARRIS AND A P-P-PAIR OF HEADPHONES CAN'T REMEDY.

NOW, SIT, UBU! SIT! GOOD DOG.
MY, HOW UNINTENTIONALLY R-R-RACIST.
RAM

THAT TRICK OF YOURS MIGHTA BROUGHT HARDY BACK ONCE. BUT DON'T COUNT ON IT WORKING NEXT TIME. NOW, MAN THE STORE! HE NEEDS ALL OUR HELP.
H-H-HELP? INTERESTING W-WORD OF CHOICE, ESPECIALLY COMING FROM YOU.

IT AMAZES ME, THE AMOUNT OF MOTHERLY H-H-HELP YOU EAGERLY GIVE TO SOMEBODY'S BLOOD SUGAR.

GRAB

AAAHHH! YOU SUNUVABITCH! GIVE IT! GIVE IT!
DIG
DIG
DIG

I'M S-SURE YOUR LUNGS APPRECIATE SUCH V-VERVE FOR WELLNESS WHEN YOU'RE NOT BURNING THROUGH A PACK A DAY!
Marlboro

OR YOUR LIVER WHEN YOU'RE NOT C-C-CORRODING IT WITH VODKA! THAT'S RIGHT, I S-SMELLED IT ON YOU THIS MORNING! LAST T-T-TIME I CHECKED, OSCILLATING BETWEEN ADDICTIONS ISN'T SOBRIETY!

OKAY, SO I CHEATED! I'M A BIG, FAT HYPOCRITE! NOW THE WHOLE WORLD CAN REST AT EASE BECAUSE YOU'VE EXPOSED THE ONLY HUMAN BEING EVER THAT F&%#S UP!
WHOOSH

CAN YOU BLAME ME, GIVEN WHAT'S REALLY AT STAKE HERE? OR DO YOU JUST HAVE TOO MUCH SALIMAH ON THE BRAIN TO F&$#IN' CARE?! AT LEAST I'M HONEST WITH MY BULLS#!T.
L-L-LOOK, I'M AWARE OF THE STAKES, ALRIGHT? BUT DON'T L-LECTURE ME ABOUT MY DISTRACTIONS!

MINE WON'T K-KILL ME LIKE DRUGS AND BOOZE. MUSIC AND ROMANCE ARE ESSENTIAL TO B-B-BEING A WELL-ROUNDED HUMAN. AND IF THERE'S SUBLIMITY AND ENLIGHTENMENT IN UNEARTHING A FORGOTTEN BUT BRILLIANT R-RECORD, THERE MUST BE IN P-POSSIBLY RECIPROCATED AFFECTION.
J-JUST LIKE THAT SONG "FEELING YOURSELF DISINTEGRATE" SAID: LOVE IN OUR LIFE IS JUST TOO V-VALUABLE TO FEEL FOR EVEN A SECOND W-WITHOUT IT.

SUNG BY THE FLAMING LIPS... WHO RIFFS ON DRUG CULTURE?

W-W-WELL, NOW YOU'RE OVERTHINKING IT!

SALIMAH'S NOT GOING ANYWHERE, MARS. YOU GOT TIME TO MAKE IT HAPPEN WITH HER. HARDY'S LOSING TIME. AND BLACKWAX WITH HIM. NOW PLEASE STAY HERE.

AS YOU W-W-WISH. I'LL ALSO KEEP THESE CIGARETTES COMPANY W-WHILE YOU'RE ABSENT. WOULDN'T WANT YOU T-TEMPTED IN THIS NEW ERA OF HONESTY.

While making **Forever Changes**, singer Arthur Lee felt he had reached the autumnal phase of his life at age 22. Convinced he was going to die soon, he etched this epitaph of elegant fatalism as his final statement. Lee would actually live until 2006, when he died of cancer at age 61. His timing was **slightly** off, but the gravestone wasn't carved in vain. As Vietnam, Chicago '68, Altamont, and the lead-punctured flesh of Dr. King and Bobby Kennedy would later demonstrate, the epitaph was for the idealism of the '60s. Change came. The dream died. But who knew death sounded so gorgeous?|

#5

LATER THAT NIGHT....

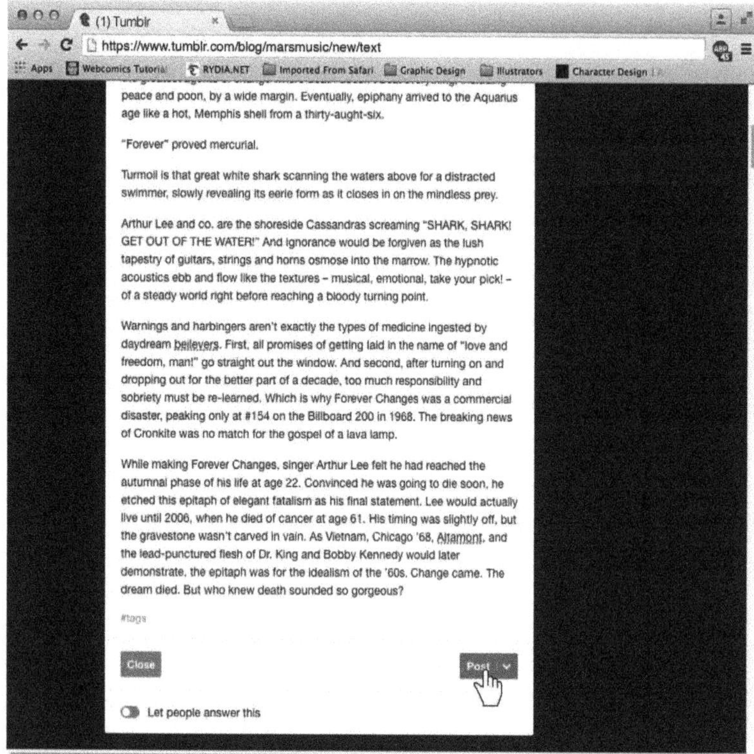

(1) Tumblr

https://www.tumblr.com/blog/marsmusic/new/text

peace and poon, by a wide margin. Eventually, epiphany arrived to the Aquarius age like a hot, Memphis shell from a thirty-aught-six.

"Forever" proved mercurial.

Turmoil is that great white shark scanning the waters above for a distracted swimmer, slowly revealing its eerie form as it closes in on the mindless prey.

Arthur Lee and co. are the shoreside Cassandras screaming "SHARK, SHARK! GET OUT OF THE WATER!" And ignorance would be forgiven as the lush tapestry of guitars, strings and horns osmose into the marrow. The hypnotic acoustics ebb and flow like the textures – musical, emotional, take your pick! – of a steady world right before reaching a bloody turning point.

Warnings and harbingers aren't exactly the types of medicine ingested by daydream beleivers. First, all promises of getting laid in the name of "love and freedom, man!" go straight out the window. And second, after turning on and dropping out for the better part of a decade, too much responsibility and sobriety must be re-learned. Which is why Forever Changes was a commercial disaster, peaking only at #154 on the Billboard 200 in 1968. The breaking news of Cronkite was no match for the gospel of a lava lamp.

While making Forever Changes, singer Arthur Lee felt he had reached the autumnal phase of his life at age 22. Convinced he was going to die soon, he etched this epitaph of elegant fatalism as his final statement. Lee would actually live until 2006, when he died of cancer at age 61. His timing was slightly off, but the gravestone wasn't carved in vain. As Vietnam, Chicago '68, Altamont, and the lead-punctured flesh of Dr. King and Bobby Kennedy would later demonstrate, the epitaph was for the idealism of the '60s. Change came. The dream died. But who knew death sounded so gorgeous?

#tags

Close Post

Let people answer this

Mars Music

http://marsmusic.tumblr.com

Follow Dashboard

Mars Music

ALBUM REVIEWS FROM THE PLANET OF GOOD TASTE

0 notes

Love's Forever Changes

"Oh, the snot has caked against my pants."

Sorry, Billy Shears, for this inconvenient truth. But the mantle for Most Important Album of the '60s belongs to Forever Changes, dreamed up by Arthur Lee and his LA-based band Love. Emerging in late fall of '67, that lysergic year where the feels were as electric as the music, Forever Changes is a nearly all-acoustic but fully prescient masterpiece that would make Janus proud. And no, dear friends, not Janis our beloved "pearl." But Janus, the Roman god of beginnings,

About the author

Greetings, interwebs!
My name is Marsalis J. Parker.
I am an English major and connoisseur of all things vinyl.
Ask me anything

Search

Blog Tools

Archive
RSS

CRAP!
I FORGOT TO MENTION WHERE THE ALBUM TITLE CAME FROM!
READERS WOULD DEFINITELY BE CURIOUS ABOUT IT!
WELL...IT'S NOT REALLY PERTINENT TO THE MAIN TOPIC. IF ANYTHING, IT'D FUNCTION AS MERELY A CUTE SIDENOTE. THE TITLE'S SURFACE MEANING IS ENOUGH FOR THEM TO UNDERSTAND THE MUSIC.
BUT WHAT ABOUT THE LYRICS?! I COULD'VE WENT MORE IN DEPTH ABOUT THEIR SOCIOPOLITICAL CONTEXT...
...BUT I COULD FILL A WHOLE BOOK ON JUST THAT ALONE AND A REDUNDANT ONE AT THAT. NO CRISIS HERE.
BESIDES, THE GRAPEVINE'S PAGE COUNT ISN'T WHAT IT USED TO BE. PITHINESS MEANS PUBLICATION...
OOH! QUOTES! WHY DIDN'T I PUT IN QUOTES FROM SOMEBODY SOMEWHERE?! SOMETHING BY ARTHUR LEE HIMSELF? OR BRYAN MACLEAN? OR THE PRODUCER?
AND WHAT ABOUT THE GROWING CREATIVE TENSION BETWEEN LEE AND MACLEAN? WHAT BETTER WAY TO EMPHASIZE TURMOIL THAN THAT?!
WHERE'S THE HIGH SCHOOL PRODIGY WHO WROTE THAT THESIS ON THE INFLUENCE OF JELLY ROLL MORTON ON MODERN BATTLE-RAPPING?
IS THIS ALL I HAVE IN ME? WHO AM I KIDDING? WHAT SELF-RESPECTING MUSIC EDITOR WOULD READ THIS INTELLECTUAL DRIVEL?!

...MOON'S A COMMON SCENE AROUND MY TOWN HERE WHERE EVERYONE IS PAINTED BROWN....
CLICK
SWIPE
SWIPE

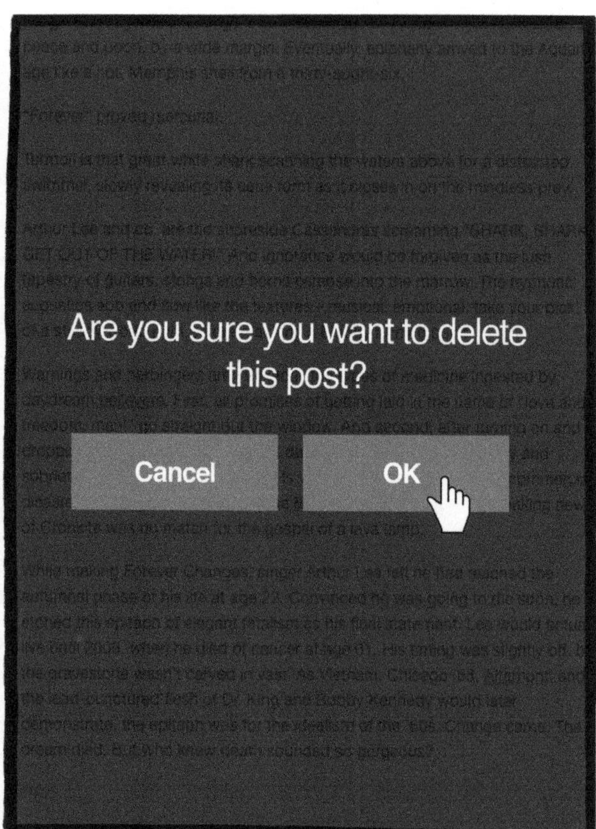
Are you sure you want to delete this post?
Cancel
OK

S-S-SORRY, MR. CHRISTGAU. *I HAVE F-F-FAILED YOU.*

Cancel
OK

BAM BAM
BAM

NIGGA, TURN DAT S#!T DOWN! MUHF#?&AS IS TRYNA SLEEP 'ROUND 'CHERE!
BAM BAM BAM
BAM
BAM

D-D-DEXTER! YOU'RE HOME ALREADY? I TH-THOUGHT YOU WERE NIGHT SHIFT.

WELL I'M, UH, OFF TONIGHT, A'IGHT?! NOW, OPEN 'NIS MUHF#?&IN' DOOR!

YOU KNOW, THE B-B-BENEVOLENCE IN YOUR VOICE IS SO *ASTRONOMICAL*, I'LL DO J-JUST THAT.

?

YOU WANNA PLAY ROUGH?! OKAY! EITHER YOU TURN DAT S#!T OFF AND LET A NIGGA SLEEP, OR ALL 'EM RECORDS YOU GOT LAYIN' AROUND IN THE LIVIN' ROOM WITH THE FUNNY-LOOKING ASIAN LETTERS ALL OVER 'EM GET PLAYED FOR MUHF$#?AS DOWN AT THE SCRAP YARD!

AAAACCKKK! NOT MY STASH OF JAPANESE VINYL PRESSINGS!

SKKKEERRRCCCHHH

D-D-DID YOU HAVE TO MAKE IT SO PER-PERSONAL?

I H-HOPE YOU FEEL LIKE A MAN NOW. I *REALLY* D-D-DO.
SHUT

T-T-TERRORIZING ***HARMLESS, INANIMATE OBJECTS*** JUST TO SAY YOU'RE T-T-TOUGH.

AND EX-XACTLY WHAT HAS MY STASH DONE TO G-G-GARNER SUCH ABUSIVE THREATS? ***ABSOLUTELY N-NOTHING, THAT'S WHAT!***

YOU KNOW, YOU RIGHT. IT AIN'T DONE NOTHING.
IT AIN'T PAY THE HEAT. IT AIN'T PAY THE RENT. AND IT AIN'T PAY THE BILLS.

IT JUST SIT AROUND AND EAT UP MORE AND MORE F#&?IN' SPACE!

J-J-JUST LIKE YOUR PORN.

AT LEAST MY S#!T COME IN SMALLER SIZES! THE HELL ELSE YOU EXPECT TO HAVE IN A BACHELOR PAD?! YOU 'MEMBA DIS MY PLACE, RIGHT?!
LOVE THOTTIES
WU-T

ONLY THE BASICS ALLOWED UP IN HERE: TV. DVD. STEREO. MICROWAVE. FRIDGE. AND DAT'S IT! JUST ENOUGH TO LIVE CHEAPLY AND ENJOY A DECENT PU$$Y RATE.

THEN YOU COME IN, TALM 'BOUT, "OH I'M ALL GRAD-JEE-ATED! I CAIN'T FIND NO JOB YET! WHERE'M I GONNA GO EAT AND WASH MY ASS NOW?!"
AND I LET YO' SORRY-LOOKING ASS MOVE IN, THINKIN' YOU GONNA GET YO' S#!T TOGETHER IN A COUPLE MONTHS.
A COUPLE MONTHS, NIGGA! NOT A COUPLE YEARS SO YOU CAN TURN MY PLACE INTO YA OWN RECORD STO'!
YOU LUCKY THE BLACK MAN HAS A LOVING HEART. OR ELSE, I'D F$#& YOU UP!

HMMM, THE B-B-BASICS. FEELS LIKE S-SOMETHING'S MISSING IN THAT WHOLE EQUATION.

DON'T I KNOW IT?! LIKE, I CAIN'T GETS NO PU$$Y NO MO'!

NO, NO. S-SIMMER DOWN, *LEVIATHAN.* I'M R-R-REFERRING TO YOUR EMPHASIS ON THE B-B-BARE NECESSITIES. THEY'RE ALL ELECTRONIC IN N-N-NATURE.
YET YOU FAIL TO GRASP THE IDEA OF *PR-PRESTIGE* AS ANOTHER NECESSITY, AS WELL AS YOUR OWN UNCONSCIOUS P-P-PURSUIT OF IT.

PRESTIGE? THE HELL DAT GOTTA DO WITH YO S#!T EATIN' UP MY PAD?

EVERYTH-THING! SEE, IT ALL ST-ST-STARTS IN *JAPAN*. AFTER WORLD WAR II, AFTER HIROSH-SH-SHIMA, JAPAN BECAME AN *ECONOMIC WASTELAND,* A LAUGHINGSTOCK TO THE FI-FI-FINANCIAL WORLD.

IT DESPERATELY SOUGHT AN *IMAGE M-MAKEOVER.* AND BY THE M-MID 1960S, IT ACHIEVED JUST THAT. SOON, JAPAN B-B-BECAME *WORLD-RENOWNED* FOR SUPERIOR QUALITY C-CAMERAS, TELEVISIONS AND STEREO EQ-Q-QUIPMENT.

AND WITH THE IMPROVEMENT OF STEREO EQ-Q-QUIPMENT CAME THE IMPROVEMENT OF *J-J-JAPANESE ALBUMS* AND THE MATERIALS USED TO MAKE THEM.

NEARLY ALL J-J-JAPANESE LPs WERE ISSUED WITH AN *'OBI'* - LITERALLY TR-TRANSLATED THIS MEANS *'SASH'* AND IS D-D-DERIVED FROM THE OBI (SASH) WORN AROUND THE
RRRRRRRRIIIIIIPPPPPPP
NIGGA, WHO GIVES A BIG, FAT S#!T ?!
AIN'T NO JAPANESE *OR* PRESTIGE PAYIN' MY MUH'F$%&IN' RENT!

IT P-P-PAID IN HOPEFULLY CONSENSUAL INTERCOURSE, CORRECT?!

TV? S-S-SONY FLATSCREEN LED. 55-INCH HIGH DEFINITION, WITH 4K R-R-RESOLUTION.

DVD? P-P-PANASONIC. BLU-RAY, STREAMING 3D WI-FI BUILT IN. HD ENABLED.
Panasonic
Blu-ray Disc

FLOOR SPEAKERS? P-P-PIONEER. 3-WAY SUBWOOFER DESIGN. 300 WATTS M-M-MAXIMUM POWER.

S-S-STAINLESS STEEL MICROWAVE AND FRENCH-DOOR FRIDGE? H-H-HITACHI! AND YOU'RE SAYING YOU B-BOUGHT ALL THIS BECAUSE YOU HAVE TO LIVE CHEAPLY?!

WELL, T-T-TWO CAN PLAY THAT GAME!
AND YOU CAN TH-THANK ME LATER.
THIS HERE C-COPY OF TUMBLEWEED CONNECTION? MADE BY T-T-TOSHIBA, WHO PRESSED ALL THEIR RECORDS ON SPECIAL RED V-VINYL THEY CALLED "EVER-CLEAN".
DESIGNED WITH A SPECIAL INGREDIENT TO P-P-PREVENT STATIC ELECTRICITY AND DUST BUILD-UP, "EVER-CLEAN" G-GIVES THIS VINYL AN INIMITABLY DIVINE LUSTER, RESULTING IN THE MOST PRI-PRI-PRISTINE SOUND HUMAN EARS HAVE EVER HEARD.
THIS IS AMONG THE MOST S-S-SOUGHT-AFTER VINYL IN THE WORLD. MUSIC FANS WILL MURDER A B-B-BABY TO ATTAIN ONE OF THESE!

ALL THE Y-Y-YEARS THEY'VE SPENT SOAKING THEIR LONELY SH-SHADOWS IN A DUSTY FACTORY OR RECORD STORE B-BASEMENT. AND ALL THE Y-Y-YEARS I'VE SPENT GIVING THEM A WARM, LOVING HOME.....
...AND NOT THROUGH EBAY, NOT THROUGH C-C-CRAIGSLIST!
DURAN DURAN
MILES DAVIS
PANGAEA
原子心母
Clash
STEREO
P-8054A

BUT THESE HANDS AND THESE F-F-FEET! SCOURING STORE AFTER STORE S-S-STORE, JUST LIKE THE P-PIONEERS! BUYING THEM ON THE CH-CHEAP WHEN NOBODY WAS LOOKING.

THE V-V-VALUE OF THESE RECORDS IS INCALCULABLE.

INCACA-WHAT?
WORTH A LOT OF M-M-MONEY.

OHHHHH.....

THEM BIG WORDS AIN'T COOL, NIGGA!

AND YOU KEEP DAT NOISE UP, OUR ASSES AIN'T GON' HAVE A WARM, LOVING HOME TO STAY IN!

THE RENT ALREADY GOT US ON **THIN ICE** WITH "THE GUTI." DON'T GIVE HER ANOTHER REASON TO F&#K OUR S#!T UP.

C-C-CORRECTION: ***YOU'RE*** ON THIN ICE WITH MRS. GUTIERREZ. SHE ***AD-D-DORES*** ME, ESPECIALLY WHEN I SPIN A LITTLE ***G-G-GAL COSTA***.

AS LONG AS YO' S#!T'S IN MY CRIB, ***SHE YO' LANDLADY TOO!***

BOOMP
BOOMP

HELLO? OPEN THE DOOR! HELLO?!
302B
BOOMP
BOOMP
BOOMP
MRS. GUTIERREZ (LANDLADY)

speak of the devil bitch.
BOOMP
BOOMP
BOOMP

you got dis. right, brotha?

W-WAIT! WHERE ARE YOU G-G-GOING?!
shhhh! as long as she ain't know I'm here, she can't bug me about the higher rent.

I KNOW YOU'RE IN THERE! YOU CAN'T FOOL ME! I CAN HEAR YOUR SALIVA DRIPPING ON THE FLOOR RIGHT NOW! ¡ABRE LA PUERTA! ¡AHORA!

uhhh...something tells me she k-k-kinda knows.

then put dat big-ass brain of yours to work and prove her wrong.

b-b-but it's pointless! she's obviously not looking for m-m-me!
Rudy

but she **ad-d-dores** you, right? get goin', nigga.

well, at least let me attain some **b-b-bottomwear**.

MIERDA.
MIERDA.
302B
CLICK

302B
UH, G-GREETINGS, MRS. GUTIERREZ.
CREEEEAAKK

WHY, MARSALIS! HOW'S MY LITTLE *PALOMO*?

WELL, THIS *DOVE* HAS SEEN B-B-BETTER DAYS.

HMM, STILL HAVEN'T HEARD BACK FROM THAT PAPER?

N-NOT YET. AND IT'S N-NOT WITHOUT EFFORT, EITHER. I'VE BEEN MAKING W-WEEKLY FOLLOW-UP CALLS FOR *FIVE WEEKS NOW.* BUT I CAN ONLY L-LEAVE A MESSAGE.
I ALSO SENT DAILY EMAILS INBETWEEN EACH C-CALL ASKING FOR P-P-POSSIBLE UPDATES.

YOU KNOW, I'M STARTING TO THINK THEY'RE AVOI-VOI-VOIDING ME.
WELLLLLL.......

B-B-BUT THAT'S WHAT'S POUNDING THE P-PAVEMENT IS ALL ABOUT, I SUPPOSE. ALL THE GR-GREATS HAVE DONE IT: ROBERT CHRISTGAU, GREIL MARCUS, CH-CH-CHESTER VICK.
PERSISTENCE IS THE MOST R-R-REQUISITE OF TRAITS A WRITER MUST P-POSSESS TO ESTABLISH HIS NAME. IT'S THE K-K-KEY TO SUCCESS.

NO, NO, NO. DUMBING IT DOWN, THAT'S THE KEY! NOBODY WANTS ARTSY-SMARTSY WRITERS. THEY'RE THE WORST!
R-R-REALLY? I KNEW MY WRITING S-SAMPLES RELIED TOO MUCH ON M-M-METAPHOR!

I'M KIDDING! OF COURSE, YOU GOTTA HAVE BRAINS IF YOU WANNA MAKE IT. WHY ARE YOU FRETTING?

F-F-FRETTING, ME? PREPOSTEROUS! I HAVE NO R-REASON TO DO SUCH A TH-TH-THING.

I R-REALLY D-DON'T.

TALENT KNOWS TALENT. THEY GOTTA BE SMART ENOUGH TO KNOW YOU CAN WRITE YOUR TUSH OFF. IF ANYBODY FRETS, SHOULD BE THAT PAPER. IT NEEDS A SMART MAN LIKE YOU.

BESIDES, CHICO, WHO ELSE IS GONNA ENLIGHTEN THESE RUGRATS TO THE GLORY OF CINEMA OLYMPIA?
HEE HEE. YEAH, THAT'S PROBABLY G-G-GAL'S BEST ONE.

AH, BUT REALLY? CHESTER VICK?! YOU ADMIRE A PIG LIKE THAT?
WELL, G-GRANTED, HIS WRITING CAN BE A TAD SEXIST.
JUST A TAD?

yeah, yeah. dat's right, nigga. talk da bitch up. then talk her out.

BUMP BUMP BA-THUMP

?

KA-PLOOOOSH

DID YOU HEAR THAT?
HEAR W-W-WHAT? I DIDN'T HEAR A TH-THING.

SOUNDS LIKE IT CAME FROM YOUR LIVING ROOM.
UHH, MUST B-B-BE ALL MY RECORDS. THEY'RE ALWAYS FALLING ALL OVER THE P-P-PLACE.

I'D BETTER T-T-TEND TO THEM. I'LL SEE YOU TOMORROW, MRS. G-G-G-

OOH OOH WAIT! JUST A SECOND! THERE WAS SOMETHING IMPORTANT I CAME UP HERE FOR. IT WAS--

S-S-SORRY IF THE MUSIC WAS TOO LOUD. IT'S OFF FOR THE N-NIGHT.

NO, NOT THAT. IT WAS...IT WAS....
AY, I'M GETTING TOO OLD TOO QUICK, CHICO.
OH, I EMPATHIZE. S-SENIORITIS IS ATTACKING US ALL. BUT A G-G-GOOD NIGHT'S REST SHOULD FIX IT. L-LATER, MRS--

YOUR BROTHER! THE RENT. HE'S OVER TWO WEEKS LATE. I NEED TO SEE HIM. NOW!

AH, S-S-SORRY, YOU J-JUST MISSED HIM. HE WENT OUT ON THE N-N-NIGHT SHIFT. HE W-W-WON'T BE BACK UNTIL M-MORNING.

HUH, STRANGE. I COULDA SWORE I JUST HEARD HIM A MINUTE AGO.

OH, TH-THAT? UH, TH-THAT WAS JUST MY, UH, MY....
302B

...MY IPHONE ON S-SPEAKER! YEAH, SOMETIMES I L-L-LEAVE IT ON S-SPEAKER WHEN I'M LISTENING TO M-MUSIC BY MYSELF. S-SOMETIMES IT CAN BE A TAD TOO L-L-LOUD.

B-B-BUT YEAH! JUST GOING THROUGH SOME OLD V-V-VOICEMAIL OF HIM RANTING ABOUT WORK AS ALWAYS. L-LONGER HOURS, P-PASSENGERS TIPPING TOO LITTLE....
SWIPE
SWIPE

AND LOVING JAPANESE ALBUMS TOO MUCH?

YEAH, THE U-U-USUAL GRIEVANCES OF A CABBIE.
I SEE NOW.

WELL, WHENEVER HE GETS BACK, SEE TO IT YOU GIVE THIS TO HIM. IT CAME THIS AFTERNOON.
PRIORITY MAIL

CITY OF GREENVILLE
TAXI & LIMOUSINE COMMISSION
122 DIXON AVE
GREENVILLE, USA
PRIORITY MAIL
DEXTER PARKER
S. 125TH ST., APT 302B
GREENVILLE, USA

MAILMAN EVEN HAD ME SIGN FOR IT. MUST BE PRETTY IMPORTANT.

SUMMONS?!
FINED FOR WHAT?!
LICENSE SUSPENSION!
PRIORITY MAIL

MUST APPEAR IN TRAFFIC COURT?!
SUMMON

MARSALIS,
YOUR TOILET IS LEAKING.

T-T-TOILET?
BUT YOU REP-PAIRED IT
TWO MONTHS AG--

BAAAAAAMM

the japanese listen to Bootsy too?
i ain't think they liked niggas.
BOOTSY?

well,
slap me
silly.

THUNK

CRACK

CLICK

OWWW! S#!T!
WHAT DA F$%K?!

A-HA! STILL LEAKING! NOTHING BUT FILTH COMIN' OUT!

YOU CRAZY-ASS MIDGET WOMAN! I TOLD YOU I'MA PAY IT!
SIX DAYS AGO! THEN THE WEEK BEFORE THAT! AND THE WEEK BEFORE THAT!
$1100! PLUS THE LATE FEES, YOU'RE TALKING $1400!

WAIT, MRS. G-G-GUTIERREZ! PLEASE, D-D-DON'T KILL HIM! YOU SEE, WE--

AAAHHHH! Q-Q-QUIT SITTING ON MY BABIES!!!

GET UP, GET UP!!! YOU'RE C-C-CRUSHING THE LIFE OUT OF THEM!

OW! NIGGA, DAMN! HOW AM I GITTIN' HIT FRONT AND BACK?!
MAYBE NEXT TIME, YOU'LL KEEP YO' S#!T IN YO' ROOM!
C-C-CUBE! P-PRODIGY! J-JACK! SPEAK TO ME!

HOW L-L-LONG WAS THAT FOUL BEAST SMOTHERING YOU? D-DON'T GO INTO THE LIGHT!

NOW LOOK AT WHATCHA DONE! JUST GIVE US ANOTHER WEEK! OUR DOLLAS IS JUST...REAL TIGHT THIS WEEK, A'IGHT?
AHHHHH, S-STILL ALIVE!

CRY ME A RIVER, *PUTO!* THE CITY'S GIVING ME ENOUGH GRIEF OVER THE HIGHER PROPERTY TAX.

HIGHER PR-PROPERTY TAX?

ADD TO THAT ALL THE BUILDING REPAIRS THEY GOT ME PAYING FOR OUTTA POCKET!

BECAUSE OF HIGHER PR-PROPERTY VALUE.

WHICH RAISES THE INSURANCE I GOT ON THIS BUILDING! WE CAN THANK ALL THOSE *TRUST-FUND KIDS* WHO KEEP MOVING IN FOR THIS MESS.

THUS, THE HIGHER R-R-RENT.

AND THE LAST THING I NEED WEIGHING ME DOWN ARE LAZY, FREELOADING TENANTS! I RUN A *BUSINESS*, NOT A *COMMUNE!* SO YOU GOT TWO CHOICES: *PAY UP* OR *PACK UP!*

WHO DA F%&K IS YOU CALLIN' LAZY, HEIFER?! YOU BEEFIN' OVER JUST TWO WEEKS!
YOU THINK A PUBLIC SERVICE OF DRIVIN' MUH'F%&KAS ALL AROUND TOWN IS FOR LAZY MUH'F%&KAS?! TWELVE-HOUR SHIFTS? 8-TO-8? ONLY SATURDAYS OFF?!
YOU NEED A NIGGA LIKE ME! THE WHOLE DAMN CITY DO! WHO ELSE GONNA TAKE YO' OLD ASS TO DA THRIFT STO' SO YOU CAN BUY ANOTHER UGLY MUH'F%$KIN' SWEATER JACKET?!
8-TO-8?
YEAH!
8 PM TO 8 AM?
HELL MUTHA'F%$KIN' YEAH!
SO IT'S ONE O'CLOCK, FRIDAY MORNING, NOW. THE HELL ARE YOU DOING HERE STILL?!

W-W-WAIT, MRS. G. T-T-TAKE THIS.

UH, MARSALIS, I'M REALLY NOT IN THE MOOD TO TALK ABOUT RECORDS RIGHT NOW.
BOWIE
DIAMOND DOGS

HOPEFULLY, YOU W-WILL AFTER I EXPLAIN. THIS IS A COPY OF *D-DIAMOND DOGS* BY DAVID BOWIE. RCA, F-F-FROM 1974. IT'S NOT C-C-CLASSIC ZIGGY, BUT CERTAINLY HAS ITS M-MOMENTS LIKE "*REBEL REBEL*", FOR EXAMPLE.
BUT, I D-DIGRESS. THIS IS ONE OF THE F-F-FIRST HANDFUL OF PRINTS SC-SCRAPPED BY RCA.
THE REASON IS THE REVERSE G-GATEFOLD, WHICH DEPICTS BOWIE WITH CANINE G-GENITALIA.
BOWIE
DIAMOND DOGS

APPARENTLY, HUMANS WITH ANIMAL P-PENISES WERE TOO HOT FOR RCA TO HANDLE. SO ALL FUTURE C-C-COPIES AIRBRUSHED IT AWAY, MAKING P-PRINTS LIKE THIS ***EXTREMELY RARE.***
HOT CANINE PEEN!
The STRANGEST LIVING
BOWIE
DIAMOND DOGS
RCA
MAINMAN

A'IGHT, FIRST OF ALL, I'MA HAFTA GIT TO URGENT CARE CUZ DIS MIDGET DONE ***F*#KED UP MY CHEEKBONE!***

AND SECOND OF ALL, ***DOG DICKS, MY NIGGA?!*** WHY WOULD A MUH'F*#KA PUT THEYSELF ON A RECORD WITH DAT S#!T ?
GO ASK THE ***C-C-COCAINE.*** 'TWAS THE '70S.
I'M STILL NOT SURE WHY YOU'RE SHOWING ME THIS.

BECAUSE M-M-MUSIC COLLECTORS WILL PAY UPWARDS OF ***4,000 D-D-DOLLARS*** FOR THAT V-VERY COVER. IN LIGHT OF BOWIE'S D-D-DEATH, MAYBE EVEN MORE. THIS SHOULD P-PAY THE NEXT COUPLE MONTHS OF R-R-RENT AND WHATEVER L-LATE FEES WE'VE RACKED UP.

AND IT SHOULD ALSO GIVE ***THE G-G-GRAPEVINE*** TIME TO TELL ME YAY OR NAY. THEY N-NEED AN ADDRESS TO R-R-RESPOND TO.

@#$!%
$%@!#!$@?
&!%$
HOLD THIS
FOR A MINUTE.
ALRIGHT.
LEMME SEE IT.
OW! THE HELL
YOU DOIN'?!
OH, HUSH.
JUST A BRUISE, YOU CRYBABY.
PUT AN ICEBAG ON IT
AND THE SWELLING'LL BE GONE
BY THE AFTERNOON.

I TH-THINK AN ICEBAG IS IN THE F-FREEZER. BE RIGHT B-B-BACK.

AY, GET DA **BUG SPRAY** WHILE YOU IN DA KITCHEN. I GOT SOME **PESTS** TO MURK.

YOU KNOW WHAT? I WILL **NEVER** UNDERSTAND HOW YOU TWO ARE BROTHERS!

HE'S THE COMPLETE OPPOSITE OF YOU! BUT I **DO** UNDERSTAND THAT YOU DON'T DESERVE A BROTHER LIKE HIM.
SOMEONE WHO'S ACTUALLY TRYING TO DO SOMETHING WITH HIS LIFE. INTELLIGENT, CARING, AMBITIOUS AND HONEST!

EVEN WHEN HE'S LYING FOR A **JERK** LIKE YOU!

AND HE'S THE ONLY REASON I'M LETTING YOU STAY FOR **TWO MORE MONTHS!**

T-T-TWO MORE MONTHS?!

AND JUST TWO! THAT'S AS FAR AS I'M ABLE TO GO. WHATEVER HAPPENS AFTER THAT FALLS ON YOU GUYS!

THANK YOU! THANK YOU! THANK YOU! THANK YOU! THANK YOU! THANK YOU!

A'IGHT, SIMMER DOWN, *URKEL!* GIMME DAT BAG ALREADY.

YOU'RE LUCKY THAT THIS *MIDGET* HAS A LOVING HEART, OR ELSE YOU'D BE SLEEPING IN A *DUMPSTER.*

ACTUALLY, WE C-COULDN'T IF WE WANTED TO R-RIGHT NOW.
THE D-DUMPSTER HOUSING MARKET IS *G-GROWING TOO FAST* TO ENTER INTO. THE HOBOS WON'T L-LEASE ONE LOWER THAN *30 D-DOLLARS* A NIGHT!

HOW DA HELL HOBOS RENTIN' OUT DUMPSTERS?!
EVEN THE HOMELESS ARE G-G-GENTRIFYING NOW.

AY, THIS WORLD! I GOTTA GET TO BED.

Y-Y-YOU ARE A TRUE *GANDALF* MRS. G. W-W-WE ARE FOREVER INDEBTED.

W-WAIT! DON'T FORGET THIS! IF YOU G-GO ON *EBAY* ASAP, YOU'LL GET AT LEAST A G-G-GOOD **4,000.**

I DON'T WANT THE RECORD, MARSALIS.

B-B-BUT, WHAT ABOUT RENT? I MEAN, YOU C-COULD EVEN PUT S-SOME OF THE MONEY LEFT OVER TO B-B-BUILDING REPAIRS.

YOU KNOW, FOR ALL THE TIME YOU'VE LIVED HERE, I DON'T THINK I EVER TOLD YOU HOW I GOT TO BE A LANDLADY.

W-WELL, NO. BUT IT S-S-SEEMS EASY TO DEDUCE. YOU PR-PROBABLY APPLIED FOR A REAL ESTATE RENTAL L-LICENSE, BOUGHT A CHEAP B-B-BUILDING, SLOWLY G-GREW YOUR WEALTH ENOUGH TO-

SHHHHHHHH. BOY, YOUR BROTHER COULD USE YOUR SMARTS.

CLICK

MY FATHER USED TO OWN THIS BUILDING. AND ONCE HE GOT TOO SICK TO RUN IT, MY MOTHER TOOK OVER. BUT IT WASN'T TOO LONG BEFORE ALZHEIMER'S TOOK OVER HER.
I WAS 22 THEN, JUST LIKE YOU. AND I WAS AN ONLY CHILD. SO I HAD TO CARRY THE BALL.

F-F-FRESH OUT OF COLLEGE TOO, EH?
MMMM. AND I PLANNED TO TAKE MY FRESH, NEW DEGREE AND BECOME A WORLD-FAMOUS FIBER ARTIST!
HAHA! IT'S Q-QUITE AN AMBITIOUS M-M-METHOD FOR PAYING OFF YOUR S-STUDENT LOANS.
OH, BUT THAT WOULD BE A CINCH AFTER ALL THE ART GRANTS AND FANCY AWARDS I WOULD WIN FOR MY BRILLIANT QUILTING!

THEN, YOU'D T-T-TRAVEL THE WORLD AND F-F-FALL IN LOVE ALONG THE WAY? M-MAYBE WITH A FRENCH POET-FILM DIRECTOR-M-MUSICIAN TYPE?

OR JUST BANG AS MANY CUTE, FOREIGN GUYS AS MY REPRESSED, CATHOLIC HORMONES ALLOWED.

BUT AS YOU CAN SEE, THIS BUILDING WAS THE LAST THING ON MY MIND. WHY STAY TIED UP AT HOME AND BE A RENTER?
W-W-WHY NOT? YOU G-GAINED A STREAM OF INCOME. SEEMS LIKE YOUR F-FATHER GAVE YOU A PR-PR-PRETTY SICK DEAL.

BUT I NEVER WORKED FOR ANY OF THIS! IT'S ALL BEEN FAMILY DUTY. ALMOST **50 YEARS** OF FULFILLING SOMEONE ELSE'S WISHES. YEAH, SURE, MONEY. FOOD ON THE TABLE. BUT I'VE LEARNED ***YOU CAN EAT AND STARVE AT THE SAME TIME.***

KEEP YOUR RECORD. CONSIDER IT AN INVESTMENT IN ***ENDING YOUR FAMINE.***

BUT THAT'S ALL I CAN DO. ***YOU*** CARRY THE BALL NOW.

METAPHORICAL F-F-FAMINE RELIEF, EH? THEN, YOU'RE NO G-GANDALF.

YOU'RE A ***G-GELDOF.***
GOOD NIGHT, PALOMO.

WAIT A MINUTE, DUDE!

WHATCHU TRIPPIN' 'BOUT? DIS AIN'T NO BRUISE. DIS A *PAYCHECK!*

PHYSICALLY ASSAULTIN' A TENANT, EMOTIONAL DISTRESS, BREACH OF QUIET ENJOYMENT. SHE F&%?IN' WIT DA HOUSIN' LAW NOW!

S#!T, WIT ALL THEM VIOLATIONS, I COULD BE LIVIN' *RENT-FREE* FOR A WHILE.

R-R-RIGHT. AND IT'S G-GOOD TIMING. BECAUSE THAT'LL FREE UP OUR YEARLY B-BUDGET...

UH, HEY! WHAT DA HELL IS DIS BULLS#!T?!
THE R-R-REASON WHY YOU'RE HOME SO EARLY, BUT THE D-DATE LISTED TELLS ME YOU ALREADY KNEW SINCE AT LEAST Y-Y-YESTERDAY MORNING.
MY OH MY, THE DISCREET CHARMS OF P-PARKING VIOLATIONS, SPEEDING T-TICKETS...
OVERCHARGING P-PASSENGERS WHILE ON AND OFF D-DUTY, HARASSMENT...
THREAT AND USE OF PHYSICAL F-F-FORCE! N-NOW, AIN'T THAT AN "EMPLOYEE OF THE MONTH"?!
23 POINTS ON YOUR N-N-NEWLY SUSPENDED LICENSE! $2,500 F-F-FINE!
AND A CURRENTLY CRASHING P-P-PU$$Y RATE.

DAT TRAITOR-ASS MANAGER!!
SO WHEN EXACTLY WERE YOU G-G-GONNA TELL ME THEY F-F-FIRED YOU? THE DAY WE MOVED INTO A D-D-DUMPSTER?!
THEY AIN'T FIRE ME! I'M JUST "OFF" FOR A WHILE.

OFF FOR 30 D-D-DAYS WITHOUT PAY?! C-C-CLOSE ENOUGH! YOU'RE RATHER FORTUNATE IT WASN'T 90 D-D-DAYS! OR FOREVER!

IF I SEE THEM MUH'F&Ø$IN' TEENAGERS AGAIN--OOOOOHHH!!! THEY GETTIN' MURKED!

YEAH, WHY DON'T YOU ADD F-F-FIRST DEGREE MURDER WHILE YOU'RE AT IT?! WITH YOUR R-R-RECORD AS IS, YOU BETTER PRAY THEY DON'T R-R-REPLACE YOU!
BRUH, I REALLY AIN'T TRYNA HEAR YO ASS RIGHT NOW!

S-S-SUCKS FOR YOU. AS DE FACTO B-B-BREADWINNER OF "YO' CRIB", I RENDER YOU CH-CH-CHOICELESS.

KEEP TALKIN' AND DIS FIST RIGHT 'CHERE FINNA RENDER YOU FACELESS!

THEN, THE COURT WILL RENDER YOU J-J-JOBLESS.

AIN'T DIS A BITCH?!
THEM MUH'F&&$&AS KNEW THE TYPE OF NIGGA I WAS WHEN THEY GAVE ME THE DAMN JOB!
SMACK

SOMETIMES, THEY EVEN HELPED ME GET AWAY WITH IT.
THE WORST PUNISHMENT WAS A TALKIN'-TO FROM DA BOSS.

IT'S BAD ENOUGH THEY GAVE ME DIS S#!T ONLY AFTER I DID MY SHIFT!
BUT NOW THEY WANNA MAIL IT TO MY HOME?!

NONE OF DIS S#!T WOULDA HAPPENED IF THE CITY AIN'T START STANNIN' RICH FOLK!
TALKIN' 'BOUT MAKIN' MORE BICYCLE LANES AND SAFER STREETS AND QUICKER TRANSIT!
NOW THESE MUH'F&&?AS WANNA MAKE A EXAMPLE OUTTA ME?!
LIKE I'M THE ONLY NIGGA DOIN' THIS S#!T?!

A'IGHT, MAYBE I AM THE ONLY NIGGA DOIN' THIS S#!T.
BUT DAT'S CUZ EVERY OTHER CABBIE'S A MUSLIM!

SNIFF
SNIFF

W-W-WAIT! DO YOU SMELL SOMETHING?

NAW. WHY YOU SMELLIN' ME?!
SNIFF
SNIFF

AHHH, THE SWEET AROMA OF V-V-VINDICATION. I COULD ADAPT TO THIS. LET THE R-RECORD SHOW IT WAS N-N-NEVER ABOUT MY MUSIC.

BUT S-S-SIMPLY ALL ABOUT YOURS. AND IT'S THE S-SAME OLD SONG WITH YOU...
...PLAYED OVER AND OVER AGAIN, EVER S-SINCE WE WERE KIDS.

A CLANGING M-M-MEDLEY OF PROJECTED AGGRESSION AND B-B-BAD JUDGMENT.

BUT ON THE P-P-POSITIVE, AT LEAST MY MUSIC GIVES LEGITIMATE PR-PR-PRESTIGE TO YOUR SEMI-FRADULENT ABODE, FINANCED BY HONEST WAGES. OH WAIT. THAT'S JUST A P-P-POSITIVE FOR ME!

ALRIGHT, KIDS. T-T-TIME FOR YOU TO HIT THE SACK. LET'S SEE, IS THIS THE *T-T-TOSHIBA* SECTION? OR *ODEON?*

UMMPHH! PERHAPS, MY N-N-NEXT INVESTMENT SHOULD BE A *B-B-BAG CART.* YOU G-G-GUYS ARE GETTING HEAVY.

"SAME OLD SONG"?
OOPS! S-SORRY, BOWIE...

WHATCHU MEAN "SAME OLD SONG"? HUH, MISTER MUSIC?

...YOU D-DON'T GO HERE, DO YOU? WELL, LET ME T-TAKE YOU AND A FEW MORE...

MISTER WRITER EXTRAORDINAIRE?

...JUST TO SET UP THE SOUNDTRACK FOR T-T-TOMORROW. OR LATER T-TODAY. YOU KNOW WHAT I MEAN.

MISTER VIRGIN?! I'MA SING YOU A SAME OLD MUH'F#$&IN' SONG!

YOU PRANCIN' 'ROUND HERE, SHOWIN' OFF YO' FANCY-ASS KNOWLEDGE, F#$%IN' WIT DEM FANCY-ASS REKKIDS, WORSHIPPIN' ALL DEM FANCY-ASS, PU$$Y-ASS, LILY-WHITE DOPE FIENDS YOU THINK ARE HIP AND COOL!
TRYNA BE KING OF DAT OLD WHITE HIPSTER BUBBLE YOU WASTE EVERYDAY IN BUT CAIN'T GET AHEAD IN. TRYNA BE DA COOLEST MUH'F#%&A ALIVE!

WELL DAMN, YA MUST BE DOIN' SOMETHIN' RIGHT! IT MUST BE DOPE TO HAVE NIGGAS LOVIN' YO' WRITIN'...
...FEELIN' ALL DAT CASH FLYIN' OUT YO' ASS...
...HAVIN' HELLA BITCHES JUMPIN' ON YO' DICK!

HOLD UP! WAIT A MINUTE!
I DON'T SEE NO NIGGAS. I DON'T SEE NO STACKS NOWHERE. AND I'D BE DA FIRST TO TELL YA WHERE DA BITCHES BE AT. WHERE DEY AT?!

OH DAT'S RIGHT! I FORGOT.

YOU AIN'T GOT S#!T 'CUZ YOU AIN'T S#!T! SILLY ME!
YOU JUST LIKE EVERY OTHER LOSER ON DA BLOCK!

BROKE.
UGLY.
BORING.
ORDINARY.
RETARDED.
REJECTED.
ALONE.

AND EITHER YOU TOO DUMB TO KNOW OR TOO CHICKENS#!T TO ADMIT...
...THAT YOU JUST AS BIG A LIAR AS I AM!

NOW, TELL ME BRUH, HOW'S DAT PR-PR-PRESTIGE WORKIN' FO' YA?!

C-C-CUTE SPEECH.

BOOMF

T-T-TECHNICALLY MEANINGLESS YET ALMOST PROFOUND IN PARTS.

YOU M-M-MIGHT ALMOST IMPRESS THE JUDGE WITH THOSE S-S-SPEAKING SKILLS.

KEE
CAL
AND
LOVE
THOT
CLICK

KE
CA
LOV
THO
AND YOU'RE W-W-WELCOME THAT I S-SAVED YOUR ASS FROM MRS. G-GUTIERREZ.

SLAM
F%#K YOU!
RAMONES

WELCOME, DEEZ NUTS! DA ONLY NIGGA I KNOW DAT HATES **NEW EDITION** THINK HE GON'... OH S#!T!

ALL DAT YAPPIN', AND DAT FOOL RUNNIN' UP DA LIGHT BILL IN HERE! **PUNK!**

KEEP CALM LOVE NO THOTTIES
CLICK

KEEP CALM LOVE NO THOTTIES

KEEP CALM LOVE NO THOTTIES

KEEP CALM LOVE NO THOTTIES
WHAT DA HELL?

DISTURBING THA PEACE PRESENTS
LUDACRIS
CHICKEN-N-BEER

WELL, I'LL BE DA DEVIL'S SON-IN-LAW! HOW HE KNOW 'BOUT MY FAVORITE JOINT OF ALL TIME?!

JACKSON... JARRETT... KIRK...
KUTI... LAWS... YUSEF LA-WHO?!

WHOOMF

DISTURBING THA PEACE PRESENTS
LUDACRIS
CHICKEN-N-BEER
WELL, YOU AIN'T BELONG HERE, BUT YOU JUST AS GOOD AS A JAPANESE REKKID TO ME.

WU-TANG
FORE DAWN
MUSIC OF YUSEF LATEEF

FORE DAWN
MUSIC OF YUSEF LATEEF

BEFORE DAWN:

INCALCULABLE, HUH?

WELL NOW, THANK YOU, L'IL BRUTHA.

THANKS A *WHOOOOOLE* LOT!

CRAP IN A HANDBASKET! HOW DID I FORGET TO DELETE MY BLOG POST?!

HOW LONG DID THAT SLOBBERING BEAST DISTRACT ME FROM MY REVIEW?!

HOW MANY USERS HAVE ALREADY BEEN EXPOSED TO MY BLAND AND SOPHOMORIC PIGSWILL?!

HOW MANY PEOPLE EVEN CARE TO READ ABOUT FOREVER CHANGES? OR KNOW WHAT GOOD MUSIC IS ANYMORE?

HOW LONG WILL I KEEP WORRYING ABOUT WHAT THEY MIGHT THINK OF ME?
SWIPE
SWIPE

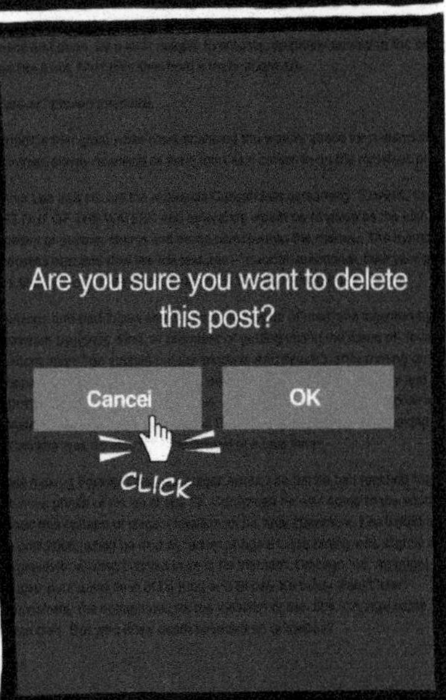
Are you sure you want to delete this post?
Cancel
OK
CLICK

1 note

r Changes

ainst my pants."

ars, for this inconvenient truth. But
Most Important Album of the '60s
ver Changes, dreamed up by Arthur
-based band Love. Emerging in late
lysergic year where the feels were as
music. Forever Changes is a nearly

About the

Greetings,
My name
I am an E
connoisse
Ask me any

Blog Too

Archive

died of cancer at age 61. His timing was slightly off, but the gravestone w
in vain. As Vietnam, Chicago '68, Altamont, and the lead-punctured flesh
and Bobby Kennedy would later demonstrate, the epitaph was for the ide
'60s. Change came. The dream died. But who knew death sounded so go

Filed under, music, folk rock, love, review, album

 **daisyagegurl** liked this and added:

| awesome review this is sooo cool =)

 **marsmusic** posted this

SHE THINKS I'M COOL?

EXTRAS

marsalis's hipster gripe #67:
SUSPENDERS

YES, S-S-SUSPENDERS! WORN BY THE SUPER-ICONOCLASTIC, SELF-DESCRIBED ***"ARTISTES"*** THAT P-P-PEPPER PLACES LIKE ***WILLIAMSBURG, B-B-BROOKLYN*** AND ***SXSW IN AUSTIN.*** TH-TH-THE ACCESSORY USED TO PROVE WITHOUT A D-D-DOUBT THAT YOU'RE SO HIP, YOU C-C-CAN'T BORROW JUST FROM THE 1980S ANY-M-M-MORE. YOU G-G-GOTTA GO TO THE ***1880S! WOW! Y-Y-YOU'RE HIPSTER AS F&#@!***

marsalis's hipster gripe #31:

EXCESSIVELY CLEVER INDIE BAND NAMES

OKAY...I G-G-GET IT. YOU BELIEVE THE WORLD OF INDIE SHOULD L-L-LAUGH AT ITSELF A LITTLE AND NOT B-B-BE SO SERIOUS. AGREED. BUT THERE ARE M-M-MORE FRUITFUL WAYS TO SHOWCASE OUR G-G-GENERATION'S PASSION FOR POP CULTURE AND W-W-WITTY NON SEQUITURS THAN JUST A ***"TWEE-AS-F#@!"*** N-N-NAME FOR YOUR BAND.
MAYBE, LIKE, UM....DUNNO. ***M-M-MAKING AN ALBUM PEOPLE WILL WANT TO REM-M-MEMBER?!***
I KNOW, TH-TH-THAT IDEA IS RATHER NOVEL.

marsalis's hipster gripe #75:
HOLOGRAM MUSICIANS
OF C-C-COURSE, I UNDERSTAND THE EMOTIONAL APPEAL OF SEEING M-MUSICAL GREATS ALIVE AGAIN THROUGH THE POWER OF TECHNOLOGY. B-BUT HERE'S MY QUESTION... WHY ARE WE WASTING THIS TECHNOLOGY ON ARTISTS N-NO LONGER WITH US, INSTEAD OF USING IT ON THE FORMER GENIUSES WHO ARE STILL HERE AND P-POLLUTING THE WORLD WITH THEIR NEWER, M-MUSICAL SWILL?!
I'D RATHER P-P-PAY $235 FOR A BONNAROO TICKET TO SEE THE STROKES WHEN THEY WERE STILL G-G-GOOD. OR THE OLD BACKPACKER K-KANYE. OR MAYBE '70S GENESIS WITH P-PETER GABRIEL.
THUG LIFE

marsalis's hipster gripe #94:

GQ MUSIC (MUSIC AS ACCESSORY)

NOW, I'M NOT C-C-CALLING ANYBODY OUT AT ALL HERE. (*COUGH* **MARK RONSON** *COUGH*) BUT ONE D-DAY, TODAY'S MUSICIANS WILL BE FORCED TO ACCEPT THAT, TEN YEARS FROM NOW, NOBODY'LL C-C-CARE ABOUT THE PANTS OR PERFUME YOU ENDORSE. ALL THAT C-CASH YOU EARNED LOOKING PRETTY WILL GO EITHER ***DOWN THE TOILET, UP YOUR NOSE OR IN YOUR V-VEIN!*** AND THE S#!TTY ALBUM YOU MADE A DECADE AGO IS NOW GOING FOR $1.50 AT ***B-B-BIG LOTS!***

hat $500
Borsalino

shirt $275
Louis Vuitton

tie $40
Alexander Olch

pants $400
Ben Sherman

jacket $875
Dries Van Noten

shoes $1000
Salvatore Ferragamo

guitar $15
First Act*

***because being a successful musician doesn't mean you won't have to cut corners somewhere**

marsalis's hipster gripe #212:

BASHING HIPSTER-BASHERS

WHAT'S YOUR MUSIC AURA?

THIS IS AN OUTRAGE!
THIS RECORD'S IN MINT CONDITION! ANY STORE WOULD KILL TO TRADE FOR THIS BABY!
FOR THE LAST TIME, O DEAR SIR, IT'S NOT ABOUT ITS CONDITION. YOU CAN'T TRADE A CRAPPY ALBUM FOR A GOOD ONE HERE! BESIDES, WE'VE BANNED KEVIN FEDERLINE.

WELL, WHAT THE HELL GIVES? I THOUGHT ALL YOU HIPSTER SHOPS JIZZED OUT OVER BAD RECORDS LIKE THIS, PART OF THAT IRONIC, OH-IT'S-SO-BAD-IT'S-GOOD MENTALITY!

SIR, THAT IS NOT A BAD RECORD. THAT'S AN UNFORGIVABLE SIN! AND YOU ARE JUST S.O.L.

REALLY? I WONDER IF YOUR MANAGER AGREES. BRING HIM HERE. NOW!

SOOOO....WHAT ALBUM IS VERONIKA AND THAT GUY?
employees only
S-S-SOMETHING AGGRESSIVE AND CONFRONTATIONAL. I'D SAY THE CLASH D-DUALLY APPLIES.

LOOK, I ***KNOW*** IT'S AWFUL. BUT MY ROOMMATE GAVE IT TO ME AS A JOKE GIFT FOR CHRISTMAS. PAWN SHOPS WON'T EVEN BUY IT OFF ME! I WILL PAY YOU ***$100*** TO JUST GET RID OF IT!

DMITRI JACKSON is an illustrator, cartoonist and teacher residing in St. Louis, Missouri.

His favorite album is
Miles Davis's In A Silent Way (1969).